Achievement in Mathematics:

Revision and Practice

Levels 1–3

M. E. Wardle and A. Ledsham

OXFORD

OXFORD

UNIVERSITY PRESS

Great Clarendon Street, Oxford OX2 6DP

Oxford University Press is a department of the University of Oxford. It furthers the University's objective of excellence in research, scholarship, and education by publishing worldwide in

Oxford   New York

Athens   Auckland   Bangkok   Bogotá   Buenos Aires   Calcutta   Cape Town   Chennai
Dar es Salaam   Delhi   Florence   Hong Kong   Istanbul   Karachi   Kuala Lumpur   Madrid
Melbourne   Mexico City   Mumbai   Nairobi   Paris   São Paulo   Singapore   Taipei
Tokyo   Toronto   Warsaw

with associated companies in   Berlin   Ibadan

ISBN 0 19 914736 1

Typeset by Tech Set, Gateshead, Tyne and Wear
Printed in Italy - G. Canale & C. S.p.A. - Borgaro T.se

CONTENTS

PREFACE

Achievement in Mathematics has been written to provide a sound foundation in the basic mathematical skills of number, measures and data handling at Levels 1–3. Each topic is introduced with a mixture of teaching and worked examples. The exercises which follow are carefully structured to enable students to work through at their own pace.

Each skill is covered on a two-page (or sometimes four-page) spread with relatively simple Level 1 questions on the left-hand page designed to develop confidence, followed by the more demanding Level 2 and Level 3 questions on the right-hand page.

The book has been specifically written for students who are following courses leading to one of the Achievement in Mathematics Awards, but it may be used by any students working at Levels 1–3 of the National Curriculum. The material is equally suitable as a course text or for revision.

The comprehensive contents list indicates each of the skills covered. This is supported by a full index and a separate Answer Book. Certain tables, diagrams and graphs have been identified with the symbol COPY⊘ . Here it may be helpful to provide the student with a photocopy to work on, rather than spend time on copying. Pages without the symbol may not be copied.

The essence of this book is simplicity and directness designed to develop the self-confidence of the student.

Michael Wardle and Alf Ledsham
January 1999

TABLES

Addition table

+	0	1	2	3	4	5	6	7	8	9
0	0	1	2	3	4	5	6	7	8	9
1	1	2	3	4	5	6	7	8	9	10
2	2	3	4	5	6	7	8	9	10	11
3	3	4	5	6	7	8	9	10	11	12
4	4	5	6	7	8	9	10	11	12	13
5	5	6	7	8	9	10	11	12	13	14
6	6	7	8	9	10	11	12	13	14	15
7	7	8	9	10	11	12	13	14	15	16
8	8	9	10	11	12	13	14	15	16	17
9	9	10	11	12	13	14	15	16	17	18

Multiplication table

x	1	2	3	4	5	6	7	8	9	10
1	1	2	3	4	5	6	7	8	9	10
2	2	4	6	8	10	12	14	16	18	20
3	3	6	9	12	15	18	21	24	27	30
4	4	8	12	16	20	24	28	32	36	40
5	5	10	15	20	25	30	35	40	45	50
6	6	12	18	24	30	36	42	48	54	60
7	7	14	21	28	35	42	49	56	63	70
8	8	16	24	32	40	48	56	64	72	80
9	9	18	27	36	45	54	63	72	81	90
10	10	20	30	40	50	60	70	80	90	100

1 Numbers

1 A *Counting*

1 How many skittles are lying down ?
2 How many skittles are standing up ?
3 How many skittles are there altogether ?
4 How many more skittles are standing up than are lying down ?

5 How many 2nd class stamps are there ?
6 How many 1st class stamps are there ?
7 How many stamps are there altogether ?
8 How many more 1st class stamps are there than 2nd class stamps ?

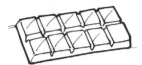 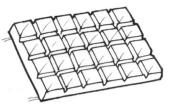

Family Bar   Giant Bar   Mini Bar

9 How many pieces of chocolate are in the Family Bar ?

10 How many pieces of chocolate are in the Giant Bar ?

11 How many pieces in the Mini Bar and Family Bar together ?

12 How many pieces in the Giant Bar and Family Bar together ?

13 How many pieces in all three bars together ?

14 How many more pieces are in the Giant Bar than in the Family Bar ?

15 How many fewer pieces are in the Mini Bar than in the Family Bar ?

16 How many pieces would there be in:

   a two Mini Bars   **b** two Giant Bars ?

one	•	1	eight	8	fifteen	15
two		2	nine	9	sixteen	16
three		3	ten	10	seventeen	17
four		4	eleven	11	eighteen	18
five		5	twelve	12	nineteen	19
six		6	thirteen	13	twenty	20
seven		7	fourteen	14	twenty-one	21

1 Write in words the numbers of dots in each pattern.

a • • •
  • • •

b • • • • •
  • • • •

2 Write in figures the number of dots in each pattern.

a • • •
  • • •
  • • •

b •
  • •
  • • •
  • • • •
  • • • • •

3 Write each number in words.

a 3   **b** 13   **c** 18   **d** 20

4 Write each number in figures.

a four   **b** seven   **c** twelve   **d** fifteen

5 Write in words:
  a the number of days in a week   **b** the number of months in a year
  c the number of players in a football team   **d** the number of 5p's in a pound (£1)

6 Write in figures:
  a the greatest possible score using a dice
  b the number of kings in a pack of cards
  c the number of cards with hearts on in a pack of cards
  d the number of days in two weeks

Examples

twenty-one	21	twenty-nine	29	one hundred and five	105
twenty-two	22	thirty-nine	39	one hundred and fifteen	115
twenty-three	23	forty-nine	49	two hundred and seven	207
twenty-four	24	fifty-nine	59	two hundred and thirty-one	231
twenty-five	25	sixty-nine	69	three hundred and forty	340

7 Write in figures the number of dots.

a ⠿ b ⠿ c ⠿ d ⠿

8 Write in words the number of dots.

a ⠿ b ⠿ c ⠿ d ⠿

9 Write in figures.

  a twenty-seven   **b** forty-two   **c** eighty

  d one hundred and three   **e** two hundred and one

  f three hundred and nineteen

10 Write in words.

  a 34   **b** 93   **c** 102   **d** 124   **e** 678

11 Write in figures:

  a the number of hours in a day

  b the number of days in January

  c the number of pence in a pound (£1)

  d the number of days in a year (not a leap year).

12 Write in words:

  a the number of days in June

  b the number of minutes in an hour

  c the number of two-pences in a pound (£1)

  d the name of a jumbo jet (747).

1 c *Place value*

23 means 2 tens and 3 units

32 means 3 tens and 2 units

30 means 3 tens and 0 units

1 a How many tens are there in 25 ?

   b How many units are there in 25 ?

2 a How many tens are there in 52 ?

   b How many units are there in 52 ?

3 How many tens are there in:
   a 27   **b** 72 ?

4 How many units are there in:
   a 27   **b** 72 ?

5 Write in figures the number which has:
   a 2 tens and 5 units   **b** 8 tens and 8 units
   c 6 tens and 0 units   **d** 0 tens and 5 units.

6 How many tens and units are in each number ?
   a 15   **b** 31   **c** 7   **d** 56   **e** 80   **f** 4

7 Which number has the most tens ?   36, 15, 42, 71, 20, 69

8 Which number has the most units ?   63, 51, 24, 17, 2, 96

9 Write in words the number 453.

The value of any figure in the number 453 depends on its place.

Hundreds	Tens	Units
4	5	3

The place value of the 4 is four hundreds, or 400.
The place value of the 5 is five tens, or 50.
The place value of the 3 is three units, or 3.

10 Write in words the number 827.

Hundreds	Tens	Units
8	2	7

11 What is the place value of the 8 in 827 ?

12 What is the place value of the 2 in 827 ?

13 What is the place value of the 7 in 827 ?

14 Write down the place value of the underlined figure.

    a 1<u>4</u>   **b** 3<u>9</u>   **c** <u>9</u>0   **d** <u>5</u>2   **e** <u>7</u>4   **f** <u>6</u>0   **g** 14<u>3</u>

    h 2<u>5</u>7   **i** <u>3</u>90   **j** 9<u>0</u>8   **k** 93<u>0</u>   **l** 7<u>4</u>1   **m** <u>5</u>0   **n** <u>5</u>

    o <u>5</u>05   **p** 5<u>5</u>0

15 Which number has the most hundreds ?
   364, 157, 421, 713, 208, 659

16 Which number has the most tens ?
   436, 715, 142, 371, 820, 569

I D *Ordering numbers*

I Which is the larger of the two numbers below ?

3   9

2 a What two-figure numbers can you make using a 3 and a 9 ?
 b Write your two numbers in order with the larger first.

3 a Which is the largest of the three numbers below ?

75   58   87

 b Which is the smallest of these three numbers ?
 c Write these three numbers in order starting with the smallest.

4 a What two-figure numbers can you make using 5's and 7's ?
 b Which is the largest of these four numbers ?
 c Which is the smallest of these four numbers ?
 d Write these four numbers in order starting with the smallest.

5 a Which is the largest of the six numbers below ?

42   28   82   84   24   48

 b Which is the smallest of these six numbers ?
 c Write these six numbers in order starting with the largest.

6 a What two-figure numbers can you make using a 1, a 5 and a 7 ?
 b Write the six two-figure numbers in order with the smallest first.
 c Write your list out again and include 11, 55 and 77.

7 a Which is the smallest of the four numbers below ?

470   740   407   704

b Which is the largest of these four numbers ?
c Write these four numbers in order starting with the smallest.

8 a What three-figure numbers can you make using 2, 5 and 5 ?
b Which is the smallest of these three numbers ?
c Which is the largest of these three numbers ?
d Write these three numbers in order starting with the smallest.

9 a Which is the largest of the six numbers below ?

471   741   417   147   714   174

b Which is the smallest of these six numbers ?
c Write these six numbers in order starting with the largest.

10 Find all the three-figure numbers that can be made with:
a 3, 8 and 9
b 2, 7 and 0
c Arrange each set of numbers in ascending order (smallest first).

2 Addition and subtraction

2 A Addition of numbers up to 10

1 Mr. and Mrs. Jones have three children.
Mr. and Mrs. Patel have two children.
  a How many adults are there in the Jones and Patel families ?
  b How many children are there in the Jones and Patel families ?
  c How many people are there in the two families together ?

2 Copy and complete:
  a $3 + 2 =$ __   **b** $5 + 4 =$ __

3 Copy and complete: $4 + 4 =$ __

4 Find:
  a $3 + 5$ **b** $1 + 7$ **c** $7 + 1$ **d** $5 + 3$

5 Copy and complete: $5 + 5 =$ __

"Find the sum of" and "Find the total of" are different ways of
saying "Add together".

6 Find the sum of:
  a 3 and 4   **b** 2 and 7   **c** 5 and 2   **d** 8 and 1

7 Find the total of:
  a 1, 2 and 3   **b** 2, 3 and 4   **c** 1, 3 and 5   **d** 3, 3 and 2

8 Use the addition square on the next page to find: $5 + 7$

9 Use the addition square to find:

  a $9 + 8$

  b $9 + 6$

  c $8 + 3$

  d $8 + 7$

  e $5 + 5$

  f $9 + 9$

+	0	1	2	3	4	5	6	7	8	9
0	0	1	2	3	4	5	6	7	8	9
1	1	2	3	4	5	6	7	8	9	10
2	2	3	4	5	6	7	8	9	10	11
3	3	4	5	6	7	8	9	10	11	12
4	4	5	6	7	8	9	10	11	12	13
5	5	6	7	8	9	10	11	12	13	14
6	6	7	8	9	10	11	12	13	14	15
7	7	8	9	10	11	12	13	14	15	16
8	8	9	10	11	12	13	14	15	16	17
9	9	10	11	12	13	14	15	16	17	18

10 Add together:

  a $9 + 5$ **b** $9 + 4$ **c** $7 + 3$ **d** $6 + 6$

11 Find the sum of:

  a 5 and 8   **b** 5 and 9   **c** 3 and 9   **d** 3 and 7

12 Find the total of:

  a 4 and 9   **b** 2 and 9   **c** 4 and 7   **d** 5 and 7

13 Find the total of:

  a 2, 5 and 8   **b** 2, 7 and 9   **c** 3, 6 and 7   **d** 3, 6 and 9

14 Copy and complete: $5 + 6 = $ ___

15 Make up three addition sums like this:

  $\square + \triangle = 11$ (The result must be eleven.)

16 Copy and complete: $2 + 4 + 6 = $ ___

17 Make up three addition sums like this:

  $\square + \triangle + * = 12$ (The result must be twelve.)

18 Copy and complete: $2 + 4 + 5 + 8 = $ ___

19 Make up three addition sums like this:

  $\square + \triangle + * + \bigcirc = 19$ (The result must be nineteen.)

2 B   *Addition problems*

1 John has 5 marbles, but he plays a game and wins 3 more.
How many marbles does he have now ?

2 Mr. Bates posts 4 first class letters and 2 second class letters.
How many letters does he post altogether ?

3 6 people are waiting at a bus stop, but before the bus comes
3 more people arrive. How many people board the bus ?

4 While I am waiting for a train I see five trains pass in one
direction and two in the other. How many trains pass altogether ?

5 There are six trees on one side of a short avenue and three on the
other. How many trees are there altogether ?

6 One morning there were seven cars in a small car park but by lunch time there were two more.
How many cars were there by lunch time ?

7 Three brothers were all good athletes. One season the numbers of trophies they won were 2, 3 and 4.
How many trophies did they win altogether ?

8 My house has 4 telephone extensions dowstairs, 2 upstairs and 1 out in the workshed. How many extensions do I have altogether ?

9 Jane's house has 4 taps in the bathroom, 4 in the kitchen and 1 outside tap. How many taps does it have altogether ?

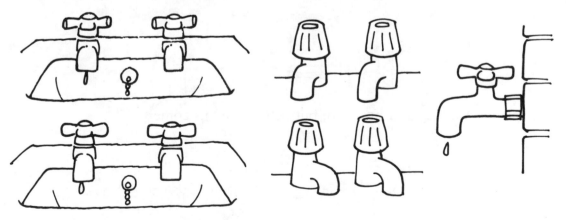

10 Three sisters are all good netball players. In one match the number of goals that they scored were 5, 2 and 2.
How many goals did they score altogether ?

11 9 men and 6 women are travelling in a minibus.
How many passengers are there altogether ?

12 A baker has 7 white loaves and 5 brown loaves on his tray.
How many loaves has he on the tray altogether ?

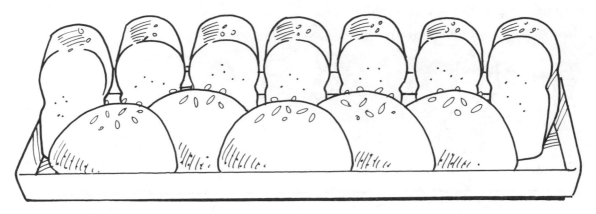

13 On a supermarket shelf there are 9 bags of plain flour and 6 bags
of self-raising flour. How many bags are there altogether ?

14 My house has 7 windows upstairs and 6 downstairs.
How many is that altogether ?

15 A cafeteria employs six people in the kitchen and five who serve
at the counter. How many employees does the cafeteria have ?

16 On a weekday nine trains stop at my local station in the northbound direction and eight in a southbound direction. How many trains stop there altogether ?

17 In Class 5A there are 7 pupils in Normans house, 6 pupils in Vikings house and 5 pupils in Saxons house. How many pupils are there in the class altogether ?

18 My pencil case contains 5 red crayons, 4 blue crayons and 2 yellow ones. How many crayons are there altogether ?

19 An office block has 5 windows at the front, 4 at the rear and 2 at one side. Find the total number of windows.

20 9 cars, 4 vans and 1 bus are waiting at the traffic lights. How many vehicles are there in the queue ?

2 c *Addition of numbers up to 20, and up to 100*

Example _____

Find: $5 + 9$

We can show this as:

	Tens	Units	
		5	i.e. five units
$+$		9	i.e. nine units
		14	i.e. fourteen units
or	1	4	i.e. one ten and four units

So $5 + 9 = 14$

_____

1 Find:

  a $2 + 9$ **b** $3 + 8$ **c** $4 + 8$ **d** $5 + 8$

2 Add together:

  a 5 and 6   **b** 6 and 7   **c** 7 and 8   **d** 9 and 4

3 Find the sum of:

  a 6 and 8   **b** 7 and 9   **c** 8 and 7   **d** 9 and 5

Example _____

Find: $13 + 15$

We can show this as:

	Tens	Units	
	1	3	i.e. one ten and three units
$+$	1	5	i.e. one ten and five units
	2	8	i.e. two tens and eight units

So $13 + 15 = 28$

_____

4 Find:

  a $12 + 15$ **b** $12 + 17$ **c** $13 + 14$ **d** $13 + 13$

5 Add together:

  a 12 and 19   **b** 17 and 19   **c** 17 and 18   **d** 17 and 13

6 Find the sum of:

  a 15 and 13   **b** 15 and 11   **c** 17 and 11   **d** 17 and 2

Example

Find: $15 + 19$

We can show this as:

	Tens	Units	
	1	5	i.e. one ten and five units
+	1	9	i.e. one ten and nine units
	2	14	i.e. two tens and fourteen units
or	2 + 1	4	
	3	4	or three tens and four units

So $15 + 19 = 34$

---

7 Find:

a $15 + 17$ **b** $15 + 18$

c $16 + 18$ **d** $16 + 17$

8 Add together:

a 12 and 19   **b** 17 and 19

c 17 and 18   **d** 17 and 13

9 Find the total of:

a 19 and 15   **b** 19 and 12

c 18 and 12   **d** 18 and 16

Example ——————————————————————

Find: $25 + 69$

We can show this as:

	Tens	Units	
	2	5	i.e. two tens and five units
+	6	9	i.e. six tens and nine units
	8	14	i.e. eight tens and fourteen units
or	8 + 1	4	
	9	4	or nine tens and four units

So $25 + 69 = 94$

——————————————————————

10 Find:

   a $25 + 67$ **b** $34 + 49$

   c $16 + 78$ **d** $34 + 57$

11 Add together:

   a 19 and 62   **b** 38 and 55

   c 26 and 34   **d** 54 and 42

12 Find the sum of:

   a 35 and 23   **b** 64 and 31

   c 47 and 5   **d** 58 and 7

Example

Find: $94 + 62$

We can show this as:

	Hundreds	Tens	Units	
		9	4	i.e. nine tens and four units
+		6	2	i.e. six tens and two units
		15	6	i.e. fifteen tens and six units
or	1	5	6	or one hundred, five tens and six units

So $94 + 62 = 156$

13 Find:

    a $94 + 42$ **b** $85 + 33$

    c $74 + 65$ **d** $68 + 50$

14 Add together:

    a 73 and 62   **b** 26 and 91

    c 87 and 36   **d** 98 and 47

15 Find the total of:

    a 62 and 99   **b** 54 and 78

    c 78 and 45   **d** 95 and 9

2 D   *Subtraction of numbers up to 10*

Example

Find: 9 take away 5

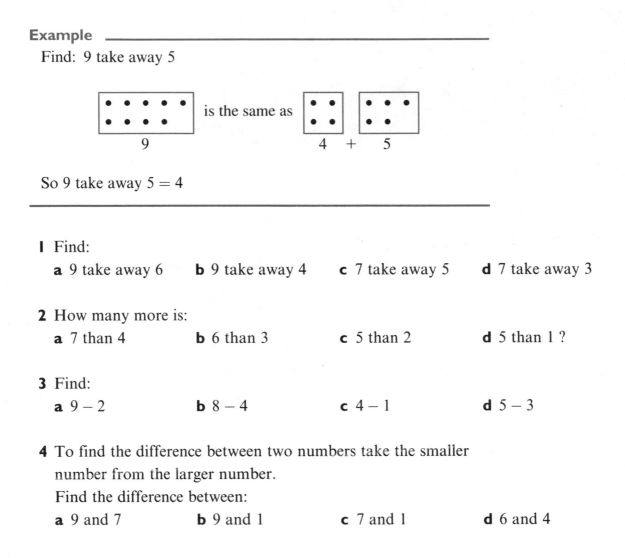

is the same as

9   4 + 5

So 9 take away 5 = 4

1 Find:

a 9 take away 6   **b** 9 take away 4   **c** 7 take away 5   **d** 7 take away 3

2 How many more is:

a 7 than 4   **b** 6 than 3   **c** 5 than 2   **d** 5 than 1 ?

3 Find:

a $9 - 2$ **b** $8 - 4$ **c** $4 - 1$ **d** $5 - 3$

4 To find the difference between two numbers take the smaller number from the larger number.
Find the difference between:

a 9 and 7   **b** 9 and 1   **c** 7 and 1   **d** 6 and 4

Find: $10 - 6$

We can think of this as what you must add to 6 to make 10.

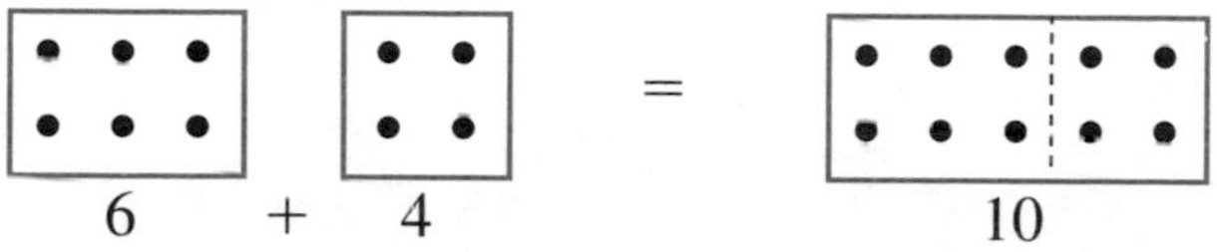

6 + 4 = 10

So $10 - 6 = 4$

---

5 What do you need to add to each number to make 10 ?

   a 7   **b** 8   **c** 2   **d** 5

6 What do you need to add to 3 to make:

   a 10   **b** 8   **c** 9   **d** 5 ?

7 Here is a subtraction sum:

$$\square - \triangle = 2$$

The $\square$ and the $\triangle$ are two different numbers.
The sum could be

$$7 - 5 = 2$$

Make up three of your own sums so that

$$\square - \triangle = 2$$

1 There are 10 passengers riding on a bus.
If 3 people get off at the next stop how many remain on board ?

2 7 people are waiting at a bus stop, but when the bus arrives it
only has room for 3 of them.
How many people must wait for the next bus ?

3 Josiah has a petrol can which holds 8 litres and it has two litres
in it.
If he takes it to a garage to fill, how many litres can he put in ?

4 I have 9 batteries in my electrical spares box, but I need 4 for my
super graphics calculator. How many batteries will be left in the
box ?

5 One afternoon a car saleroom has 7 cars on show but the
salesman sells 4 of them before the evening.
How many cars are still for sale ?

6 A train consists of 10 coaches, but 4 are detached at one station en route. How many coaches are left on the train ?

7 Suzie has a set of encyclopaedias which consist of 10 volumes, but she can only find 7 of them.
How many volumes are still missing ?

8 There are 9 houses in Short Street. If the postman delivers mail to only 6 of them one morning, how many houses did not receive any mail ?

9 Marlon needs 10 stakes to build a fence, but he only has 2.
How many stakes must he buy ?

10 9 people are waiting in a dentist's waiting room, some for treatment and some for check-ups. If 2 are waiting for a check-up, how many are waiting for treatment ?

2 F *Subtraction of numbers up to 20, and up to 100*

Example _____

Find 12 take away 4

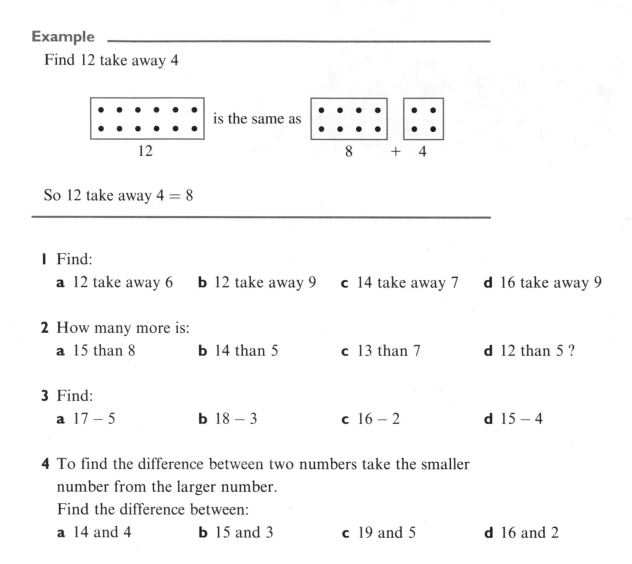

is the same as

12

8 + 4

So 12 take away 4 = 8

_____

I Find:

    a 12 take away 6   **b** 12 take away 9   **c** 14 take away 7   **d** 16 take away 9

2 How many more is:

    a 15 than 8   **b** 14 than 5   **c** 13 than 7   **d** 12 than 5 ?

3 Find:

    a 17 − 5   **b** 18 − 3   **c** 16 − 2   **d** 15 − 4

4 To find the difference between two numbers take the smaller
number from the larger number.
Find the difference between:

    a 14 and 4   **b** 15 and 3   **c** 19 and 5   **d** 16 and 2

Example ————————————————————

Find: 18 − 13

We can show this as:

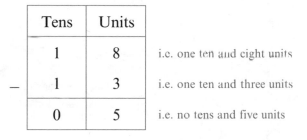

Tens	Units
1	8
1	3
0	5

i.e. one ten and eight units

i.e. one ten and three units

i.e. no tens and five units

So 18 − 13 = 5

————————————————————

5 Find:

  a 18 − 15   **b** 18 − 13   **c** 19 − 11   **d** 16 − 12

6 Work out:

  a 19 take away 13   **b** 19 take away 15

  c 14 take away 11   **d** 15 take away 10

7 Find the difference between:

  a 15 and 13   **b** 19 and 16   **c** 18 and 14   **d** 13 and 10

Example _____

Find: $69 - 24$

We can show this as:

	Tens	Units	
	6	9	i.e. six tens and nine units
−	2	4	i.e. two tens and four units
	4	5	i.e. four tens and five units

So $69 - 24 = 45$

_____

8 Find:

  a $69 - 32$ **b** $87 - 53$ **c** $76 - 24$ **d** $59 - 27$

9 How many more is:

  a 76 than 24   **b** 86 than 63   **c** 57 than 12   **d** 96 than 25 ?

10 Find the difference between:

  a 87 and 26   **b** 58 and 42   **c** 76 and 56   **d** 97 and 30

Example

Find: $64 - 29$

We can show this as:

	Tens	Units	
	6	4	i.e. six tens and four units
$-$	2	9	i.e. two tens and nine units

This can be thought of as:

	Tens	Units	
	$5 + 1$	4	i.e. five plus one tens and four units
$-$	2	9	i.e. two tens and nine units

Which can be written as:

	Tens	Units	
	5	14	i.e. five tens and fourteen units
$-$	2	9	i.e. two tens and nine units
	3	5	i.e. three tens and five units

So $64 - 29 = 35$

---

11 Find:

  a $64 - 39$ **b** $72 - 38$ **c** $85 - 59$ **d** $94 - 25$

12 Find the difference between:

  a 74 and 29   **b** 70 and 36   **c** 54 and 9   **d** 81 and 7

1 What note (£10, £20 or £50) would you need to buy:
   a the tie   **b** the skirt   **c** the jacket ?

2 **a** Is 13 rounded to 10 or to 20 ?
   b Is 28 rounded to 20 or to 30 ?
   c Is 66 rounded to 60 or to 70 ?
   d Is 75 rounded to 70 or to 80 ?

Rule: When approximating to the nearest 10,
75 is rounded to 80.

3 Approximate each number to the nearest 10.
   a 12   **b** 23   **c** 59   **d** 65

4 Express each number correct to the nearest 10.
   a 18   **b** 27   **c** 51   **d** 75

5 Round each number to the nearest 10.
   a 36   **b** 52   **c** 85   **d** 93

6 Jim weighs 48 kg and his sister Jane weighs 32 kg.
   Express their weights correct to the nearest 10 kg.

7 The distance from London to Aylesbury is 59 km
   and the distance from London to Guildford is 44 km.
   Approximate these distances to the nearest 10 km.

8 a Is 130 rounded to 100 or to 200 ?

  b Is 280 rounded to 200 or to 300 ?

  c Is 660 rounded to 600 or to 700 ?

  d Is 450 rounded to 400 or to 500 ?

Rule: When approximating to the nearest 100,
we round 450 up to 500.

9 Approximate each number to the nearest 100.

  a 120   **b** 230   **c** 590   **d** 650

10 Express each number correct to the nearest 100.

  a 180   **b** 270   **c** 510   **d** 750

11 Round each number to the nearest 100.

  a 360   **b** 520   **c** 850   **d** 930

12 a Is 138 rounded to 130 or to 140 ?

  b Is 297 rounded to 290 or to 300 ?

  c Is 661 rounded to 660 or to 670 ?

  d Is 505 rounded to 500 or to 510 ?

13 Approximate each number to the nearest 10.

  a 123   **b** 238   **c** 594   **d** 605

14 Approximate each number to the nearest 100.

  a 186   **b** 248   **c** 551   **d** 975

15 A kitten weighs 618 grams. Give her weight correct to the nearest:

  a 10 grams   **b** 100 grams.

16 One pint of milk has a volume of 568 cubic centimetres.
Express this volume correct to the nearest:

  a 10 cubic centimetres   **b** 100 cubic centimetres.

2 H *Addition and subtraction using a calculator*

I Write these calculator numbers in words:

   a 2   **b** 4   **c** 78   **d** 95

2 How would your calculator display:

   a three   **b** twenty-four   **c** sixty-three   **d** ninety ?

3 Press the following buttons on your calculator:

   AC 3 + 5 = . Did you get the answer 8 ?

4 Use your calculator to find:

   a $2 + 7$ **b** $4 + 3$ **c** $5 + 8$ **d** $7 + 9$

5 Press the following buttons on your calculator:

   AC 9 − 4 = . Did you get the answer 5 ?

6 Use your calculator to find:

   a $7 - 2$ **b** $6 - 3$ **c** $8 - 5$ **d** $9 - 2$

7 Now press: AC 2 3 + 1 9 = .
   Did you get the answer 42 ?

8 Now press: AC 9 1 − 2 3 = .
   Did you get the answer 68 ?

9 Use your calculator to find:

   a $46 + 23$ **b** $57 + 36$ **c** $62 - 37$ **d** $54 - 35$

Use your calculator for each of the following.

10 Find the change from a £10 note for:

    a a box of chocolates which costs £2   **b** a box of toffees which costs £4.

11 Find the change from a £20 note for:

    a a pair of slippers which costs £6   **b** a pair of shoes which costs £9.

12 Find the change from a £50 note for:

    a a table which costs £29   **b** a chair which costs £14.

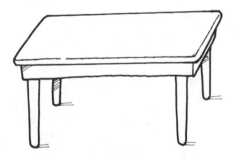

13 In Class 8B there are 15 girls and 9 boys.
How many pupils are there in the class altogether ?

14 Marcus arrived at the bus stop 9 minutes before his bus was due,
but when the bus came it was 12 minutes late.
For how many minutes did he have to wait altogether ?

15 Theresa went to the newsagent's shop and paid 45p for a
newspaper, 35p for a comic and 8p for a pencil.
How much did she spend altogether ?

I Find the distance from Leeds to Hull.

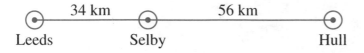

2 Josiah weighs 63 kg and his sister Kanika weighs 39 kg. If they stand on a weighing machine together, what will the reading be ?

3 32 people are sitting downstairs on a bus and 29 are sitting upstairs. If there are no standing passengers, how many people are travelling on the bus altogether ?

4 My local station has only two platforms. If 28 people are waiting on one platform and 23 on the other, how many people are waiting altogether ?

5 A car park has two levels. If 45 cars are parked on the lower level and 35 on the upper level and there are no spare spaces, how many cars can the park accommodate altogether ?

6 In a cafeteria 49 people are sitting at the tables and 16 people are waiting in the queue.

How many customers are in the cafeteria altogether ?

7 A ferry boat can carry 40 cars, but on one sailing there are only 24 on board.

How many empty spaces are there ?

8 A bus depot houses 30 buses, but on one particular day 9 stayed in the depot for repairs.

How many were out in service ?

9 A local football league has 24 member clubs. If 8 of them play in striped shirts, how many of them play in plain shirts ?

10 By mistake Julian arrived one hour (sixty minutes) early for a theatre show. The doors, however, did open 35 minutes before the show started.

How long did he have to wait outside ?

11 One day at a nursery school 63 pupils arrived on time, 15 arrived on a late-running minibus and 7 were absent.
How many pupils did the school have altogether ?

12 One day a very full bus had 26 passengers travelling in the downstairs seats, 31 travelling in the upstairs seats and 5 more standing downstairs. How many people were on the bus altogether ?

13 A motorway bus runs from Birmingham to Worcester. It leaves Birmingham bus station with 25 passengers, picks up 16 more at Edgbaston and 11 more at Bearwood. If no passengers get off en route, how many leave the bus at Worcester ?

14 Find the distance from Newcastle to Berwick. Also give your answer:
a correct to the nearest 10 km
b correct to the nearest 100 km.

Berwick

46 km

Alnwick

34 km

Morpeth

27 km

Newcastle

15 A short branch-line train consists of a locomotive of weight 56 tonnes, a coach of weight 31 tonnes and a parcels van of weight 29 tonnes. Find the total weight of the train.
Also give your answer correct to the nearest:
a 10 tonnes   **b** 100 tonnes.

16 Mrs. Gray buys a new cabinet (£73), a microwave oven (£95) and a kettle (£13) for her kitchen. Find how much she spends altogether. Also give your answer correct to the nearest:
   a £10   **b** £100.

17 Ronnie, Zoey and Charmaine pick some blackberries. If they pick 50, 65 and 70 grams respectively, what weight do they pick altogether ? Also give your answer to the nearest:
   a 10 grams   **b** 100 grams.

18 Wayne buys a pair of trousers (£9) and a shirt (£4).
   What will be his change if he pays with a £20 note ?

19 Deena buys a coat (£24) and a blouse (£7).
   What will be her change if she pays with a £50 note ?

20 A cinema has seats for 100 people.
   a If 35 people are sitting on one side of the aisle and 32 on the other, how many empty seats are there ?
   b If there are 50 seats on each side, how many empty seats are there on each side ?

2 J *Solving problems (1)*

1 What number do we have to add to 3 to make 8 ?

2 Find the missing number:
  a $3 + \_\_ = 7$ **b** $5 + \_\_ = 8$

3 Find the missing number:
  a $\_\_ + 3 = 8$ **b** $\_\_ + 3 = 9$ **c** $\_\_ + 5 = 8$ **d** $2 + \_\_ = 7$

4 What number do we have to subtract from 8 to make 5 ?

5 Find the missing number:
  a $8 - \_\_ = 3$ **b** $8 - \_\_ = 6$ **c** $9 - \_\_ = 4$ **d** $7 - \_\_ = 1$

6 What number do we have to subtract 3 from to make 5 ?

7 Find the missing number:
  a $\_\_ - 3 = 4$ **b** $\_\_ - 3 = 2$ **c** $\_\_ - 5 = 4$ **d** $\_\_ - 6 = 2$

8 What number do we have to add to 13 to make:
  a 18   **b** 28 ?

9 Find the missing number:
  a $13 + \_\_ = 17$ **b** $15 + \_\_ = 18$

10 Find the missing number:
  a $13 - \_\_ = 7$ **b** $32 - \_\_\_ = 17$

11 What number do we have to subtract from 13 to make 5 ?

12 Find the missing number:
  a $\_\_\_ - 10 = 25$ **b** $\_\_\_ - 8 = 15$

Questions **13** and **14** begin with the phrase "I think of a number".
For each question find the numbers thought of.

13 a I add 7 to it and the result is 15.
   b I add 15 to it and the result is 32.

$? \longrightarrow \boxed{+\,7} \longrightarrow 15$

14 a I subtract 5 from it and the result is 12.
   b I subtract 15 from it and the result is 15.

$? \longrightarrow \boxed{-\,5} \longrightarrow 12$

15 a What must I do to 8 to get 13 ?
   b What must I do to 15 to get 24 ?

$8 \longrightarrow \boxed{?} \longrightarrow 13$

In Questions **16** to **18** fill in the missing box in the flow-chart.

16 $\boxed{?} \longrightarrow \boxed{+\,3} \longrightarrow \boxed{+\,3} \longrightarrow 9$

17 $\boxed{?} \longrightarrow \boxed{-\,2} \longrightarrow \boxed{-\,2} \longrightarrow 0$

18 $8 \longrightarrow \boxed{+\,7} \longrightarrow \boxed{?} \longrightarrow 10$

19 My dog weighs 31 kg, my cat weighs 6 kg and when I stand on
the scales with them both the reading is 100 kg.
What is my weight ?

20 I drive from Liverpool to Hull via Manchester and Leeds and my
car's mileometer shows 130 miles.

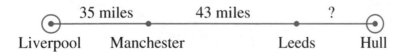

How far is it from Leeds to Hull ?

37

3 Multiplication and division

3 A Idea of multiplication

1 Mrs. Gray buys two boxes of six eggs.
How many eggs does she buy altogether ?

2 Mrs. Patel buys three boxes of six eggs.
How many eggs does she buy altogether ?

3 What is three lots of five ?

4 Find three lots of:
   a 2   **b** 7

5 What is 4×5 or four times five ?

6 What is 5×4 ?

7 Find four times:
   a 4   **b** 7

8 Do you agree that 3 lots of four is the same as 4 lots of three ?

9 Copy and complete: $4 + 4 + 4 = 3 \times$ __ or __ $\times 3$

10 Use the multiplication table to find:

   a 8×5 **b** 8×7

   c 9×6 **d** 9×8

   e 6×5 **f** 6×6

   g 7×1

×	1	2	3	4	5	6	7	8	9
1	1	2	3	4	5	6	7	8	9
2	2	4	6	8	10	12	14	16	18
3	3	6	9	12	15	18	21	24	27
4	4	8	12	16	20	24	28	32	36
5	5	10	15	20	25	30	35	40	45
6	6	12	18	24	30	36	42	48	54
7	7	14	21	28	35	42	49	56	63
8	8	16	24	32	40	48	56	64	72
9	9	18	27	36	45	54	63	72	81

11 Multiply:

   a 4×7 **b** 6×9

12 Find the product of:

   a 5×9 **b** 6×8

In Questions **13** to **15** find some numbers to fill in the empty boxes to make up the multiplications.

13 Make up three multiplication sums like this: $3 \times \square = \square$

14 Make up three multiplication sums like this: $\square \times 4 = \square$

15 Make up three multiplication sums like this: $\square \times \square = 12$
(The result must be 12.)

16 Find:

   a $2 \times 3 \times 4$ **b** $2 \times 4 \times 5$ **c** $3 \times 3 \times 8$ **d** $3 \times 3 \times 5$

3 B   *Multiplication by 2 and by 5*

1 Find:

   a 3 + 3   **b** 4 + 4   **c** 7 + 7   **d** 9 + 9

2 Now write down:

   a 2×3 **b** 2×4 **c** 2×7 **d** 2×9

3 Mrs. Gray buys two books of four stamps.
   How many stamps does she buy altogether ?

4 Mrs. Patel buys two bags of six oranges.
   How many oranges does she buy altogether ?

5 Find:

   a 2 + 2 + 2 + 2   **b** 2 + 2 + 2 + 2 + 2 + 2

6 Write down the next five numbers in the sequence:
   2, 4, 6, _, _, _, _, _

7 Find:

   a 5 + 5   **b** 5 + 5 + 5   **c** 5 + 5 + 5 + 5   **d** 5 + 5 + 5 + 5 + 5

8 Write down the next four numbers in the sequence:
   5, 10, 15, _, _, _, _

9 Mrs. Ahmed has five children. They each invite two friends to a
   party. How many children are there at the party altogether ?

10 Mrs. Siam has five cats. Each cat eats seven tins of cat food a
   week. How many tins do they eat altogether each week ?

3 c *Multiplying any number by 10*

1 Find:

   a $10 + 10$ **b** $10 + 10 + 10$ **c** $10 + 10 + 10 + 10$

2 Write down:

   a 2×10 **b** 3×10 **c** 4×10

3 Write down the next five numbers in the sequence:

   10, 20, 30, _, _, _, _, _

4 Multiply each number by 10:

   a 3   **b** 5   **c** 8   **d** 10

5 First class stamps can be sold in books of ten.
   How many stamps will there be in:

   a 4 books   **b** 6 books ?

6 Garden canes are sold in bundles of ten sticks.
   How many canes will there be in:

   a 3 bundles   **b** 8 bundles ?

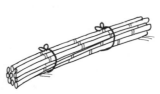

7 How many tens are there in:

   a 60   **b** 100 **?**

Tens	Units
6	0

There are six tens in 60

   c 160   **d** 190

Hundreds	Tens	Units
1	6	0

There are sixteen tens in 160

8 Multiply each number by 10:

   a 13   **b** 18   **c** 30   **d** 60
   e 90   **f** 23   **g** 56   **h** 87

9 How many tens are there in:

   a 250   **b** 690 ?

3 D *Multiplication of numbers up to 20, and up to 100*

Example

Find: 13×4

We can show this as:

	Tens	Units	
	1	3	
$\times$		4	
	1	2	(3×4)
$+$	4	0	(10×4)
	5	2	(13×4)

So $13 \times 4 = 52$

---

1 Find:

   a 12×4 **b** 16×4 **c** 19×4 **d** 15×4

2 Multiply together:

   a 13 and 6   **b** 17 and 6   **c** 14 and 6   **d** 15 and 6

3 Find:

   a 30×4 **b** 40×4 **c** 70×4

   d 20×4 **e** 60×6 **f** 90×7

Example ──────────────────────────────

Find: 53×7

We can show this as:

	Hundreds	Tens	Units	
		5	3	
$\times$			7	
		2	1	(3×7)
$+$	3	5	0	(50×7)
	3	7	1	(53×7)

So $53 \times 7 = 371$

──────────────────────────────

4 Find:

   a 52×7 **b** 63×7 **c** 39×6
   d 25×9 **e** 32×9 **f** 73×4

5 Find the missing number:

   a $60 \times \underline{\quad} = 240$ **b** $80 \times \underline{\quad} = 560$

   c $90 \times \underline{\quad} = 540$ **d** $50 \times \underline{\quad} = 450$

6 Find the missing number:

   a $\underline{\quad} \times 4 = 320$ **b** $\underline{\quad} \times 7 = 420$

   c $\underline{\quad} \times 8 = 720$ **d** $\underline{\quad} \times 4 = 60$

7 Find:

    a 20×30 **b** 20×40 **c** 30×30

    d 30×40 **e** 40×60 **f** 70×90

Example

Find: 27×30

We can show this as:

	Hundreds	Tens	Units	
		2	7	
$\times$		3	0	
	2	1	0	(7×30)
$+$	6	0	0	(20×30)
	8	1	0	(27×30)

So $27 \times 30 = 810$

8 Find:

    a 24×30 **b** 23×40 **c** 36×70

    d 42×90 **e** 33×50 **f** 26×50

Find: 63×14

We can show this as:

	Hundreds	Tens	Units	
		6	3	
$\times$		1	4	
		1	2	(3×4)
	2	4	0	(60×4)
		3	0	(3×10)
$+$	6	0	0	(60×10)
	8	8	2	(63×14)

So $63 \times 14 = 882$

9 Find:

   a 26×14 **b** 37×13 **c** 43×15

   d 47×18 **e** 24×15 **f** 35×16

10 Find the missing number:

   a $16 \times \underline{} = 160$ **b** $32 \times \underline{} = 320$

   c $\underline{} \times 10 = 930$ **d** $\underline{} \times 10 = 600$

11 Find the missing number:

   a $30 \times \underline{} = 600$ **b** $40 \times \underline{} = 800$

   c $50 \times \underline{} = 1500$ **d** $50 \times \underline{} = 1000$

1 8 boys go blackberry picking. If they each pick 3 pounds, how many pounds do they pick altogether ?

2 Batteries for Paul's calculator are sold in packets of 4.
If he buys 3 packets, how many batteries does he buy ?

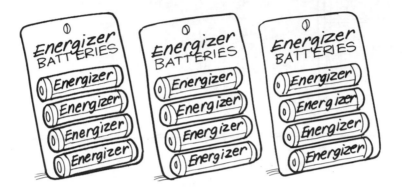

3 There are 7 text books in a pile on a class teacher's desk.
If each book is 2 cm thick, how high is the pile of books ?

4 Jane buys 6 packets of grapefruits. If there are 4 in each packet, how many grapefruits does she buy altogether ?

5 There are 9 shops in a shopping centre. If each shop employs 5 people, how many people work at the shopping centre altogether ?

6 A book cabinet has 4 shelves. If there are 9 books on each shelf, how many books are there in the cabinet altogether ?

7 Peter buys 6 hinges for a pair of cupboard doors. If each hinge has 6 screw holes, how many screws will he require ?

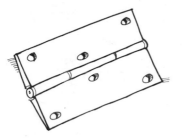

8 A box of tiddly-winks has 8 red ones, 8 blue ones, 8 green ones and 8 yellow ones. How many tiddly-winks are there altogether ?

9 At Highmead School there are 17 pupils in each of the 4 classes in Year Nine.

How many pupils are there in Year Nine altogether?

10 An excursion train has every seat occupied.

If each coach holds 52 people and the train consists of 5 coaches, how many people are travelling on the train?

11 Find the distance from London to Bristol.

12 A path consists of flagstones laid in a straight line.

If each stone is 54 cm in length and 10 are required, what is the length of the path?

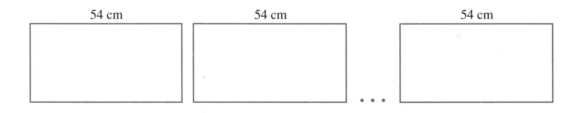

13 Cartons of orange squash are despatched in wholesale boxes of 48. If a cafe buys 10 wholesale boxes, how many cartons do they buy ?

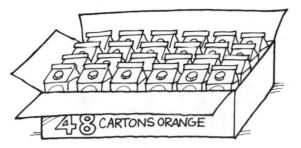

14 A necklace consists of 45 beads. If each bead measures 10 millimetres across, how long is the necklace ?

15 A packet contains 15 biscuits, but a box of the same biscuits contains 12 times as many.
How many biscuits are there in the box ?

16 18 teams play in a league of rugby teams.
If on one Saturday all the teams are playing, find the total number of players if there are 15 in each team.

3 F   *Idea of division*

I Mrs. Gray buys six Choco bars.
She shares them between her two children.
How many bars will each child receive ?

2 Mr. Louiso buys twelve bottles of wine.
He shares them between himself and three work colleagues.
How many bottles will each person receive ?

3 How many times will 3 go into 12 ?

4 What is 12 ÷ 3 ?

5 How many times will 3 go into:
   a 6   **b** 15 ?

6 What is 12 ÷ 6 ?

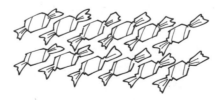

7 How many groups of 4 can be made from:
   a 8   **b** 20 ?

8 Copy and complete:
   a 8 ÷ 2 =   **b** 9 ÷ 3 =   **c** 15 ÷ 3 =   **d** 18 ÷ 6 =

9 Use the multiplication table to find:

   a $18 \div 3$ **b** $28 \div 4$ **c** $15 \div 5$

   d $56 \div 7$ **e** $40 \div 8$ **f** $63 \div 9$

×	1	2	3	4	5	6	7	8	9
1	1	2	3	4	5	6	7	8	9
2	2	4	6	8	10	12	14	16	18
3	3	6	9	12	15	18	21	24	27
4	4	8	12	16	20	24	28	32	36
5	5	10	15	20	25	30	35	40	45
6	6	12	18	24	30	36	42	48	54
7	7	14	21	28	35	42	49	56	63
8	8	16	24	32	40	48	56	64	72
9	9	18	27	36	45	54	63	72	81

10 Divide:

   a 14 by 7   **b** 72 by 8   **c** 45 by 9   **d** 48 by 6

11 Find how many groups of 6 can be made from:

   a 12   **b** 30   **c** 54   **d** 36

In Questions **12** to **15** find some numbers to fill in the empty boxes to make up the divisions.

12 Make up three division sums like this: $24 \div \square = \square$

13 Make up three division sums like this: $\square \div 3 = \square$

14 Make up three different division sums like this: $\square \div \square = 4$
   (The result must be 4.)

15 Make up three different division sums like this: $\square \div \square = 9$
   (The result must be 9.)

16 Find:

   a $72 \div 9$ **b** $54 \div 9$ **c** $64 \div 8$ **d** $16 \div 4$

17 Divide:

   a 81 by 9   **b** 49 by 7   **c** 48 by 8   **d** 35 by 7

3 G   *Odd and even numbers*

I Write down the next five numbers in this sequence:
2, 4, 6, 8, _, _, _, _, _

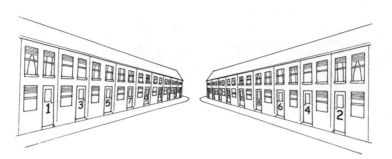

These are called the **even** numbers. They are all divisible by 2

2 Write down the next five numbers in this sequence:
1, 3, 5, 7, _, _, _, _, _

These are called the **odd** numbers.

3 Say whether the number is an **odd** number or an even number:
  a 5   **b** 8   **c** 22   **d** 99

4 Say whether the number is divisible by 2 or not:
  a 4   **b** 7   **c** 19   **d** 76

5 Write down the next four numbers in this sequence:
5, 10, 15, _, _, _, _

6 Say whether the number is divisible by 5 or not:
  a 10   **b** 25   **c** 52   **d** 70

7 Write down the next four numbers in this sequence:
10, 20, 30, _, _, _, _

8 Say whether the number is divisible by 10 or not:
  a 10   **b** 25   **c** 50   **d** 113

3 H   *Division by 10*

1 Write down:

  a 5×10 **b** 7×10

2 How many tens are there in:

  a 70   **b** 100 ?

3 Divide each number by 10:

  a 30   **b** 80

4 Tea bags can be sold in boxes of 40. If these are shared amongst 10 people, how many does each person receive ?

5 Write down:

  a 15×10 **b** 19×10

6 How many tens are there in:

  a 150   **b** 190 ?

7 Divide each number by 10:

  a 120   **b** 140

8 Write down:

  a 20×10 **b** 70×10

9 How many tens are there in:

  a 200   **b** 700 ?

10 Divide each number by 10:

  a 300   **b** 500

11 How many tens are there in:

  a 250   **b** 470   **c** 730   **d** 910 ?

12 Divide each number by 10:

  a 230   **b** 340   **c** 980   **d** 460

3 I *Division of numbers up to 20, and up to 100*

Example

Find: $68 \div 4$

We can show this as:

	Tens	Units
or $4)$	6	$^{2}8$
	1	7

$4 \times 10 = 40$

$4 \times 7 = 28$

so $4 \times 17 = 68$

So $68 \div 4 = 17$

1 Find:

a $48 \div 4$ **b** $96 \div 3$ **c** $64 \div 4$ **d** $91 \div 7$

2 Find:

a $38 \div 2$ **b** $54 \div 3$ **c** $60 \div 4$ **d** $72 \div 6$

3 Divide 96 by:

a 2 **b** 3 **c** 6 **d** 8

Example

Find $156 \div 13$

We can show this as:

	Hundreds	Tens	Units
or 13	) 1	$^{1}5$	$^{2}6$
	0	1	2

$13 \times 10 = 130$

$13 \times 2 = 26$

so $13 \times 12 = 156$

So $13 \times 12 = 156$

4 Find:

a $156 \div 12$ **b** $272 \div 16$ **c** $252 \div 14$

d $288 \div 12$ **e** $336 \div 16$ **f** $364 \div 14$

5 Divide 960 by:

a 8 **b** 15 **c** 30 **d** 40 **e** 80 **f** 4

6 Find the missing number:

a $60 \div __ = 15$ **b** $84 \div __ = 7$ **c** $96 \div __ = 8$ **d** $60 \div __ = 12$

e $__ \div 4 = 18$ **f** $__ \div 7 = 60$ **g** $__ \div 8 = 50$ **h** $__ \div 6 = 25$

Example _____

Mrs Jones' hens lay 16 eggs.

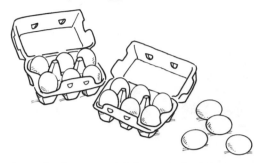

She puts these in boxes which each hold 6 eggs. She fills 2 boxes and has 4 eggs left over.

Note: 6 goes into 16 two times with 4 left over.
We say that $16 \div 6 = 2$ with a remainder of 4.

_____

7 What is the remainder when:
   a 48 is divided by 5   **b** 7 is divided by 3
   c 65 is divided by 7   **d** 43 is divided by 8 ?

8 What is the remainder when:
   a 110 is divided by 12   **b** 140 is divided by 15
   c 108 is divided by 13   **d** 147 is divided by 16 ?

9 Say what the remainder is when the number is divided by 13:
   a 100   **b** 500   **c** 800   **d** 900

10 Find:
   a $240 \div 20$ **b** $360 \div 40$ **c** $420 \div 70$ **d** $390 \div 30$

Find $529 \div 23$

We can show this as:

```
         2  3
23 ) 5   2  9
    -4   6        (23 × 20)
     6   9
   -     6  9     (23 × 3)
     0   0
```

$$23 \times 20 = 460$$
$$23 \times 3 = 69$$
$$\text{so } 23 \times 23 = 529$$

So $529 \div 23 = 23$

11 Find:

    a $483 \div 21$ **b** $624 \div 26$ **c** $980 \div 28$

    d $851 \div 23$ **e** $612 \div 36$ **f** $702 \div 39$

12 Divide 896 by:

    a 8   **b** 14   **c** 56   **d** 64

13 Find the missing number:

    a $315 \div \_\_ = 45$ **b** $315 \div \_\_ = 105$ **c** $\_\_ \div 12 = 60$ **d** $\_\_ \div 25 = 24$

3 J *Division problems*

1 Mrs. Jones has a box of chocolates with 18 chocolates inside it. If she shares them out equally between her 3 children, how many does each one receive ?

2 20 people are waiting at a taxi rank and all are going to the same place. If 5 taxis are required to move them, how many people can ride in each taxi ?

3 Peter sends for 18 minature light bulbs for his Christmas tree. When they arrive he finds that there are 6 small packets of bulbs in the parcel. How many bulbs are there in each packet ?

4 An urban motorway is 16 kilometres long and has five equally spaced access points. Find the distance between any pair of access points.

5 Kanika has 28 kg of flour. She finds that it fills 7 exactly similar bags. How many kilograms does each bag hold ?

6 Levi has a string of sausages of length 63 cm. If there are 7 sausages in the string, how long is each sausage ?

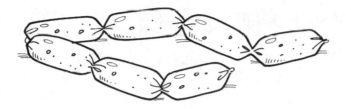

7 A piece of wood is 96 cm long. If it is cut up into six equal lengths, how long is each part ?

8 6 identical biscuits are placed on the kitchen scales and the dial reads 84 grams. What is the weight of each biscuit ?

9 A farmer has 91 kg of grain and he has to place it into 8 kg sacks. How many sacks will he fill and how many kilograms will be left over ?

10 A nurse has 79 millilitres of a certain medicine. If each of her patients require 5 millilitres, how many patients can she treat and how many millilitres will be left over ?

11 An art teacher has a packet containing 96 sheets of paper. If she shares the sheets out between 7 pupils, how many sheets will each pupil receive and how many sheets will be left over ?

12 Zoey has a piece of tape which is 80 cm long. If she cuts it into 6 equal parts, how long will each part be and what length will be left over ?

13 A milkman has 900 bottles of milk on his float and they exactly fill 36 crates. How many bottles does each crate hold ?

14 A wooden gate is 300 cm wide. It is made from boards which are 15 cm wide.

How many of these boards were required to make the gate ?

15 A new school orders 700 desks. If they are equally distributed between 25 classrooms, how many desks are in each classroom ?

16 Marcus has a toy train which has a circular track of length 384 cm.

If the circle is made from 12 curved rails, how long is each rail ?

1 Press the following buttons on your calculator:
[AC] [3] [×] [5] [=] . Did you get the answer 15 ?

2 Use your calculator to find:
   a 2×7 **b** 5×8

3 Press the following buttons on your calculator:
[AC] [2] [0] [÷] [4] [=] . Did you get the answer 5 ?

4 Use your calculator to find:
   a $14 \div 2$ **b** $80 \div 5$

5 Now press: [AC] [2] [3] [×] [1] [9] [=] .
Did you get the answer 437 ?

6 Now press: [AC] [5] [2] [9] [÷] [2] [3] [=] .
Did you get the answer 23 ?

7 Use your calculator to find:
   a 36×23 **b** 78×85 **c** $560 \div 35$ **d** $777 \div 37$

8 a Do you agree that $123 \times 456 = 56\,088$?
   b What is the largest number you can make using a
      multiplication sum like this but rearranging the six figures ?

3 L *Solving problems (2)*

1 What number do we multiply 3 by to make 18 ?

2 Find the missing number:

    a $3 \times \underline{\quad} = 21$ **b** $5 \times \underline{\quad} = 45$ **c** $5 \times \underline{\quad} = 60$ **d** $6 \times \underline{\quad} = 90$

3 What number when multiplied by 3 makes 24 ?

4 Find the missing number:

    a $\underline{\quad} \times 3 = 21$ **b** $\underline{\quad} \times 6 = 48$ **c** $\underline{\quad} \times 5 = 70$ **d** $\underline{\quad} \times 7 = 98$

5 What number do we divide into 24 to make 8 ?

6 Find the missing number:

    a $24 \div \underline{\quad} = 3$ **b** $36 \div \underline{\quad} = 9$ **c** $135 \div \underline{\quad} = 15$ **d** $140 \div \underline{\quad} = 35$

7 What number do we have to multiply by 13 to make 143 ?

8 a $13 \times \underline{\quad} = 52$ **b** $13 \times \underline{\quad} = 78$ **c** $12 \times \underline{\quad} = 180$ **d** $15 \times \underline{\quad} = 255$

9 What number do we have to divide into 840 to make 140 ?

10 Find the missing number:

    a $840 \div \underline{\quad} = 40$ **b** $725 \div \underline{\quad} = 29$ **c** $900 \div \underline{\quad} = 20$ **d** $360 \div \underline{\quad} = 30$

3 M *Multiplication and division problems*

1 It takes Mr. Khan 12 minutes to travel to work and Mr. Simpson 4 times as long. Mr. Simpson takes 3 times longer than Miss Carr. How long does it take:
a Mr. Simpson   **b** Miss Carr to travel to work ?

2 David weighs 28 kg and his father is 3 times as heavy. His father is 7 times as heavy as his baby sister Mary. How heavy is:
a David's father   **b** Mary ?

3 Peter has 24 marbles and Anit has five times as many. Anit has six times as many marbles as Ayo. How many marbles has:
a Anit   **b** Ayo ?

4 Reading is 54 km from London and the distance from Reading to Newport is three times as far. This distance is nine times the distance from Newport to Cardiff.
Find the missing distances on the map.

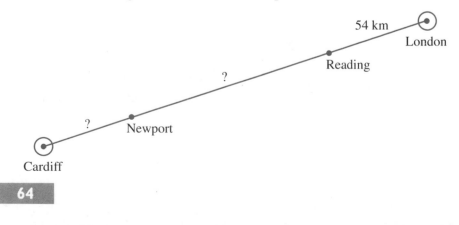

5 48 people live in West Street and five times as many live in North Street. In North Street there are 4 times the number of people as in East Street. How many people live in:

a North Street   **b** East Street ?

6 It takes James 54 minutes to travel to school, and this is 3 times longer than it takes Susan. Jean, however, takes 4 times longer to travel to school than Susan. Find the time it takes:

a Susan   **b** Jean to travel to school.

7 A bottle contains 60 headache tablets, and this is 5 times the number in a paper packet. A tin of the same tablets, however, contains 8 times as many as the paper packet. Find the number of tablets in:

a the paper packet   **b** the tin.

8 Tom scored 42 goals for his football team last season, and this was 3 times as many as Sanjay. Ronnie, the top scorer, however, scored 4 times as many as Sanjay. Find the number of goals scored by:

a Sanjay   **b** Ronnie.

9 West Park School has children of all ages. The junior department has 136 pupils which is 4 times as many as the infant department. If the senior department has 7 times as many pupils as the infant department, how many pupils are there in:

a the infant department

b the senior department ?

10 The distance from London to Taunton is 228 kilometres, which is 6 times as far as from Taunton to Exeter. If the distance from Exeter to Plymouth is twice as far as the distance from Taunton to Exeter, find the distances from:

a Taunton to Exeter

b Exeter to Plymouth.

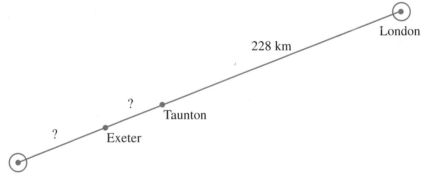

11 Shani's school has 1350 pupils and this is 50 times as many as the number of pupils in Shani's class. In Shani's house, however, there are 12 times as many pupils as there are in her class. Find the number of pupils in:

a Shani's class

b Shani's house.

12 360 people are sitting in the standard class seats on a train and this is 15 times as many as the number who are sitting in the buffet car. There are, however, 11 times as many people sitting in the first class seats as in the buffet car.

Find how many passengers are sitting in:

a the buffet car

b the first class seats.

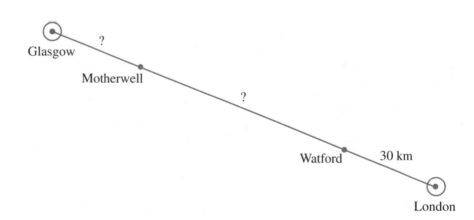

13 The distance from London to Watford is 30 km. The distance from Watford to Motherwell is 20 times as far. This is 25 times the distance from Motherwell to Glasgow. Find the distances from:

a Watford to Motherwell

b Motherwell to Glasgow.

Glasgow

?

Motherwell

?

Watford   30 km

London

14 One afternoon many people went from their village to a nearby beach. 40 of them cycled, but 15 times as many went by car and the number who went by car was also 25 times greater than the remaining number who walked. How many people:

a went by car

b walked ?

4 Sequences

4 A Recognising and continuing simple patterns

I Draw the next three shapes in the pattern below.

2 Draw the next three shapes in the pattern below.

3 Draw the next three shapes in the pattern below.

4 Draw the next three shapes in the pattern below.

5 What sort of numbers are these: 2, 4, 6, 8, 10 ?
Write down the next five numbers in the sequence.

6 What sort of numbers are these: 1, 3, 5, 7, 9 ?
Write down the next five numbers in the sequence.

7 What sort of numbers are these: 3, 6, 9, 12, 15 ?
Write down the next five numbers in the sequence.

8 What sort of numbers are these: 7, 14, 21, 28, 35 ?
Write down the next five numbers in the sequence.

9 Write down the next three letters in the sequence:
A, C, E, G, I

10 Write down the next three letters in the sequence:
A, D, G, J, M

11 Write down the next three letters in the sequence:
A, Z, B, Y, C

12 Write down the next six numbers in the sequence:
1, 2, 4, 5, 7, 8

13 Write down the next six numbers in the sequence:
1, 1, 2, 3, 3, 4

14 Write down the next six numbers in the sequence:
1, 2, 10, 3, 4, 20

15 Draw the next three shapes in the pattern below:

16 Draw the next three shapes in the pattern below:

4 B *Finding the next terms in a sequence*

I Write down the next number in each sequence.
  a 4, 8, 12, 16, 20   **b** 99, 97, 95, 93, 91
  c 4, 7, 10, 13, 16   **d** 2, 7, 12, 17, 22

2 Write down the next letter in each sequence.
  a B, D, F, H, J   **b** Y, W, U, S, Q
  c D, G, J, M, P   **d** C, G, K, O, S

3 Write down the next number in each sequence.
  a 1, 4, 9, 16, 25   **b** 1, 2, 4, 7, 11
  c 1, 3, 6, 10, 15   **d** 2, 3, 5, 8, 13

4 Draw the next three shapes in each sequence.

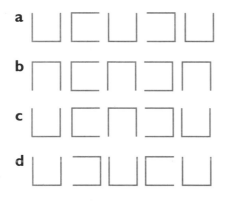

5 Draw the next three shapes in each sequence.

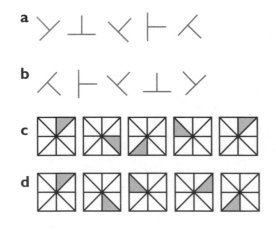

4 c *Predicting a particular term in a sequence*

1 Do you agree that the seventh term of the sequence below is 14 ?
2, 4, 6, 8, 10
What is:
a the tenth term of this sequence.
b the twentieth term of this sequence ?

2 Do you agree that the seventh term of the sequence below is 13 ?
1, 3, 5, 7, 9
What is:
a the tenth term of this sequence.
b the twentieth term of this sequence ?

3 Do you agree that the seventh term of the sequence below is 20 ?
2, 5, 8, 11, 14
What is:
a the tenth term of this sequence.
b the twentieth term of this sequence ?

4 a Draw the next four terms of the sequence below:

b Name three other terms which will be the same as:
   i the fourth term   **ii** the fifth term   **iii** the sixth term.

5 Money

5 A Coins: simple totals

1 Find the total for each set of coins.

a 1p, 1p, 1p, 1p, 1p, 1p

b 1p, 2p, 1p, 2p, 1p, 2p

c 1p, 2p, 5p, 5p, 2p, 1p

2 Find the total for each set of coins.

a 5p, 5p, 5p, 10p, 10p, 10p

b 1p, 2p, 5p, 10p, 20p, 50p

c 50p, 20p, 20p, 5p, 2p, 2p

3 Find the total for each set of coins:

a 50p, 20p, 10p, 10p, 10p, 5p

b 50p, 50p, 20p, 20p, 10p, 10p

c 50p, 50p, 20p, 10p, 10p, 5p

d 50p, 50p, 20p, 20p, 20p, 10p

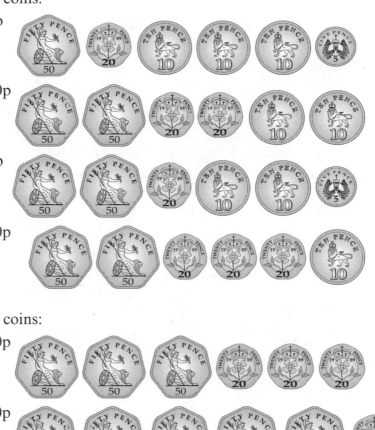

4 Find the total for each set of coins:

a 50p, 50p, 50p, 20p, 20p, 20p

b 50p, 50p, 50p, 50p, 50p, 20p

c 50p, 50p, 50p, 50p, 20p, 10p

d 50p, 50p, 50p, 50p, 20p, 20p

For questions **5** and **6** list all the possible ways of paying. All or some of the given coins may be used.

5 An eraser costs 9p. There are eight ways of paying if 5p, 2p and 1p coins are available.

6 A large bag of crisps costs 60p. There are five ways of paying if 50p, 20p and 10p coins are available.

5 B *Converting p to £ and £ to p*

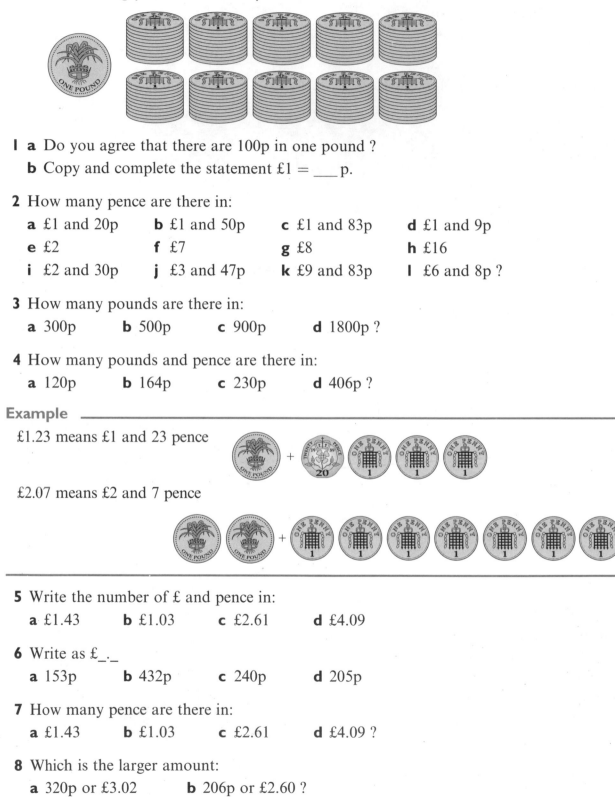

1 a Do you agree that there are 100p in one pound ?

  b Copy and complete the statement £1 = ___ p.

2 How many pence are there in:

  a £1 and 20p   **b** £1 and 50p   **c** £1 and 83p   **d** £1 and 9p

  e £2   **f** £7   **g** £8   **h** £16

  i £2 and 30p   **j** £3 and 47p   **k** £9 and 83p   **l** £6 and 8p ?

3 How many pounds are there in:

  a 300p   **b** 500p   **c** 900p   **d** 1800p ?

4 How many pounds and pence are there in:

  a 120p   **b** 164p   **c** 230p   **d** 406p ?

Example

£1.23 means £1 and 23 pence

£2.07 means £2 and 7 pence

5 Write the number of £ and pence in:

  a £1.43   **b** £1.03   **c** £2.61   **d** £4.09

6 Write as £_._

  a 153p   **b** 432p   **c** 240p   **d** 205p

7 How many pence are there in:

  a £1.43   **b** £1.03   **c** £2.61   **d** £4.09 ?

8 Which is the larger amount:

  a 320p or £3.02   **b** 206p or £2.60 ?

5 c   *Finding the numbers of 2p, 5p and 10p in sums of money*

1 How many 2p's are there in 10p ?

2 How many 5p's are there in 10p ?

3 How many 10p's are there in 20p ?

4 How many 2p's are there in 20p ?

5 How many 5p's are there in 20p ?

6 How many 10p's are there in:
   a 50p   **b** £1 ?

7 How many 2p's are there in:
   a 8p   **b** 14p   **c** 64p   **d** 96p ?

8 How many 5p's are there in:
   a 15p   **b** 30p   **c** 75p   **d** 90p ?

9 How many 2p's are there in:
   a 50p   **b** £1 ?

10 How many 5p's are there in:
   a 50p   **b** £1 ?

5 D *Totals and change from £1, £5 and £10*

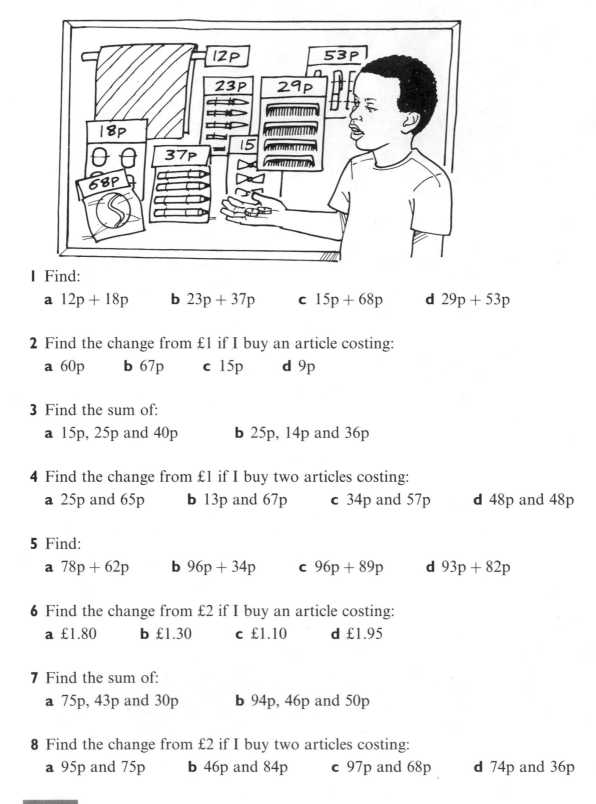

1 Find:

   a 12p + 18p   **b** 23p + 37p   **c** 15p + 68p   **d** 29p + 53p

2 Find the change from £1 if I buy an article costing:

   a 60p   **b** 67p   **c** 15p   **d** 9p

3 Find the sum of:

   a 15p, 25p and 40p   **b** 25p, 14p and 36p

4 Find the change from £1 if I buy two articles costing:

   a 25p and 65p   **b** 13p and 67p   **c** 34p and 57p   **d** 48p and 48p

5 Find:

   a 78p + 62p   **b** 96p + 34p   **c** 96p + 89p   **d** 93p + 82p

6 Find the change from £2 if I buy an article costing:

   a £1.80   **b** £1.30   **c** £1.10   **d** £1.95

7 Find the sum of:

   a 75p, 43p and 30p   **b** 94p, 46p and 50p

8 Find the change from £2 if I buy two articles costing:

   a 95p and 75p   **b** 46p and 84p   **c** 97p and 68p   **d** 74p and 36p

9 Find:

   a £1.27 + £1.53   **b** £1.42 + £1.58

10 Find the change from £5 if I buy an article costing:

   a £1.27   **b** £2.36   **c** £3.98   **d** £4.92

11 Find:

   a £1.27 + £1.83   **b** £1.86 + £2.58

12 Find the change from £5 if I buy two articles costing:

   a £1.40 and £1.90   **b** £1.89 and £2.44

13 Find:

   a £5.32 + £2.98   **b** £4.96 + £2.39

14 Find the change from £10 if I buy an article costing:

   a £7.35   **b** £8.15   **c** £5.53   **d** £9.08

15 Find:

   a £3.10 + £2.55 + £1.90   **b** £4.12 + £1.67 + 89p

16 Find the change from £10 if I buy two articles costing:

   a £3.75 and £4.45   **b** £8.29 and £1.66

5 E *Addition and subtraction of money*

Example ──────────────────────────────

Find: £1.13 + £2.38

We can show this as:

	£	p	
	1	13	i.e. £1.13
+	2	38	i.e. £2.38
	3	51	

So £1.13 + £2.38 = £3.51

───

I Find:

  a £1.25 + £1.50   **b** £1.37 + £2.21

  c £2.83 + £3.12   **d** £3.24 + £2.63

2 Add together:

  a £1.12 and £3.69   **b** £1.25 and £2.37   **c** £2.57 and £4.29   **d** £3.79 and £2.15

Example ──────────────────────────────

Find: £1.43 and £2.85

We can show this as:

	£	p	
	1	43	i.e. £1.43
+	2	85	i.e. £2.85
	3	128	i.e. £3 and 128p
or	4	28	i.e. £4.28

So £1.43 + £2.85 = £4.28

───

3 Find:

  a £1.35 + £1.83   **b** £1.72 + £2.84

  c £2.95 + £3.82   **d** £3.71 + £4.93

4 Find the sum of:

  a £2.51 and £5.69   **b** £5.08 and £1.93

  c £2.36 and £6.94   **d** £2.02 and £4.98

Example _____

Find: £3.38 − £2.13

We can show this as:

	£	p	
	3	38	i.e. £3.38
−	1	13	i.e. £1.13
	1	25	i.e. £1.25

So £3.38 − £2.13 = £1.25

_____

5 Find:

   a £3.75 − £1.50   **b** £7.96 − £2.62

   c £8.75 − £1.43   **d** £9.87 − £6.24

6 Subtract:

   a £1.12 from £3.69   **b** £6.16 from £8.98

   c £6.52 from £7.96   **d** £3.20 from £8.57

Example _____

Find: £3.45 − £1.62

We can show this as:

		£	p	
		3	45	i.e. £3.45
	−	1	62	i.e. £1.62
or		2	145	i.e. £2 and 145p
	−	1	62	i.e. £1.62
		1	83	i.e. £1.83

So £3.45 − £1.62 = £1.83

_____

7 Find:

   a £4.35 − £1.93   **b** £5.49 − £1.76

   c £8.17 − £2.93   **d** £6.06 − £3.54

8 Find the difference between:

   a £6.51 and £2.69   **b** £9.36 and £2.79

   c £7.30 and £1.86   **d** £5.00 and £1.76

5 F *Multiplication and division of money*

Example ───────────────────────────────

Find: £3.21 × 4

We can show this as:

```
            £      p
            3     21
       ×           4
                  84   (21p × 4)
       +  12      00   (£3 × 4)
          12      84   £(3.21 × 4)
```

So £3.21 × 4 = £12.84

───

1 Find:

   a £4.13 × 4   **b** £5.32 × 3   **c** £3.22 × 4   **d** £4.21 × 4

2 Multiply:

   a £2.34 by 2   **b** £1.22 by 4   **c** £2.21 by 4   **d** £2.30 by 3

Example ───────────────────────────────

Find: £2.53 × 7

We can show this as:

```
            £      p
            2     53
       ×           7
                  21   (3p × 7)
                 350   (50p × 7)
       +  14      00   (£2 × 7)
          14     371   (£14 and 371p)
    or    17      71   (i.e. £17.71)
```

So £2.53 × 7 = £17.71

───

3 Find:

   a £2.41 × 7   **b** £3.62 × 4   **c** £5.93 × 2   **d** £4.31 × 5

4 Multiply:

   a £3.56 by 2   **b** £2.75 by 3   **c** £6.46 by 4   **d** £3.48 by 5

Find: £4.28 ÷ 4

We can show this as:

$4 \times £1 = £4$

$4 \times 7p = 28p$

so $4 \times £1$ and $7p = £4.28$

So £4.28 ÷ 4 = £1.07

```
      £    p
4 ) 4    28
    1    07
```

---

5 Find:

  a £4.48 ÷ 4   **b** £6.93 ÷ 3   **c** £6.48 ÷ 2   **d** £9.66 ÷ 3

6 Divide £12.96 by:

  a 2   **b** 3   **c** 4   **d** 6

Example _____

Find: £7.28 ÷ 4

We can show this as:

```
              £      p
              1     82
      4  )  7     28
          - 4           (4 × £1)
            3     28
      or          328
                 -320    (4 × 80p)
                    8
                   -8    (4 × 2p)
                    0
```

So £7.28 ÷ 4 = £1.82

---

7 Find:

  a £5.28 ÷ 4   **b** £4.62 ÷ 3   **c** £8.58 ÷ 3   **d** £9.08 ÷ 4

8 Divide £5.76 by:

  a 2   **b** 3   **c** 8   **d** 9

9 Divide £6.30 by:

  a 2   **b** 3   **c** 7   **d** 9

10 Share £16.45 equally between 5 children.

5 G *Using a calculator with money*

1 Press the following buttons on your calculator:

AC 1 · 2 3 + 4 · 5 6 =

Did you get the answer 5.79 ? What is £1.23 + £4.56 ?

2 Use your calculator to find:

   a £2.31 + £1.65   **b** £3.54 + £4.37

   c £7.34 + £4.95   **d** £4.73 + 36p (£0.36)

3 Press the following buttons on your calculator:

AC 4 · 5 6 − 1 · 2 3 =

Did you get the answer 3.33 ? What is £4.56 − £1.23 ?

4 Use your calculator to find:

   a £2.87 − £1.65   **b** £6.54 − £4.37

   c £5.17 − £2.89   **d** £7.34 − £4.95

5 Use your calculator to find:

   a £2.31 + £1.11 − £1.25   **b** £3.54 + £4.34 − £2.17

   c £5.17 + £2.12 − £3.15   **d** £7.34 + £4.94 − £2.19

6 Press the following buttons on your calculator:

$\boxed{AC}$ $\boxed{1}$ $\boxed{\cdot}$ $\boxed{2}$ $\boxed{3}$ $\boxed{\times}$ $\boxed{3}$ $\boxed{=}$

Did you get the answer 3.69 ? What is £1.23 × 3 ?

7 Use your calculator to find:

    a £2.31 × 3   **b** £3.54 × 2   **c** £5.17 × 4   **d** £4.29 × 6

8 John buys 3 shirts costing £12.99 each. What is his total bill ?

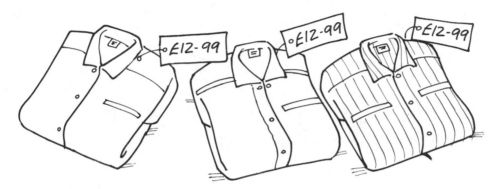

9 Press the following buttons on your calculator:

$\boxed{AC}$ $\boxed{3}$ $\boxed{\cdot}$ $\boxed{6}$ $\boxed{9}$ $\boxed{\div}$ $\boxed{3}$ $\boxed{=}$

Did you get the answer 1.23 ? What is £3.69 ÷ 3 ?

10 Use your calculator to find:

    a £8.43 ÷ 3   **b** £3.54 ÷ 2   **c** £7.35 ÷ 5   **d** £6.72 ÷ 8

11 Afiya buys 9 pads of art paper for £13.50.
How much does one pad cost ?

5 H *Shopping*

For questions **1** to **5** find:

a the total paid

b the change from £1.

1 Jim buys an eraser (18p), a pencil (14p) and a jotter (53p).

2 Michelle buys a ruler (21p), a set square (34p) and a protractor (40p).

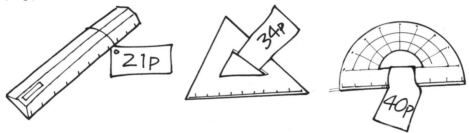

3 Wendy buys 3 small jotters which cost 24p each.

4 Bobbie buys 4 packets of chewing gum which cost 19p each.

5 Naomi buys 5 coloured biros which cost 14p each.

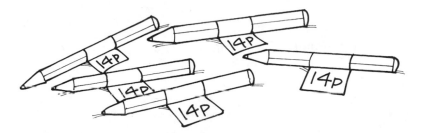

6 Ayo buys a packet of 4 oranges which costs 92p.
What is the price of each orange ?

7 Josiah buys a packet of 3 fruit pies which costs 87p.
What is the cost of each pie ?

8 Kanika buys a packet containing 5 red candles which costs 90p.
What is the cost of each candle ?

For questions **9** to **13** find:

a the total paid

b the change from £10.

9 Julian buys a screwdriver (£1.65), a hammer (£2.70) and a folding rule (£2.15).

10 Rebecca buys a pair of sunglasses (£3.50), a tube of toothpaste (£2.25) and a packet of vitamin tablets (75p).

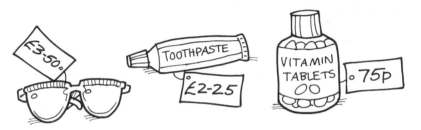

11 Tnisha buys a magazine (£1.35), a newspaper (35p) and a comic (65p).

12 Marcus buys 5 electric plugs costing £1.36 each.

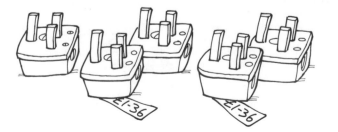

13 Kyante buys 4 choc ices costing 85p each.

14 Candace buys a packet containing 5 light bulbs for £6.25.
What is the cost of each light bulb ?

15 Shani buys 4 super power batteries for £5.40.
What is the cost of each battery ?

16 Suzanne buys 6 loaves of bread for £3.90.
What is the cost of each loaf ?

6 Time

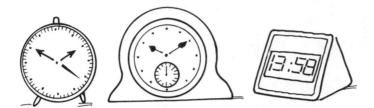

1 There are 60 minutes in 1 hour. How many minutes are there in:
   a 4 hours   **b** 7 hours   **c** 10 hours ?

2 How many hours are there in:
   a 180 minutes   **b** 300 minutes   **c** 540 minutes ?

3 There are 60 seconds in 1 minute. How many seconds are there in:
   a 5 minutes   **b** 3 minutes   **c** 15 minutes ?

4 How many minutes are there in:
   a 420 seconds   **b** 240 seconds   **c** 600 seconds ?

5 How many seconds are there in 60 minutes ?

6 How many seconds are there in 1 hour ?

7 Copy and complete the table:

	Hours	Minutes	Seconds
a		480	
b		600	
c			10 800
d			18 000
e	9		
f	12		
g	$\frac{1}{2}$ an hour		
h	$\frac{1}{4}$ of an hour		

6 B   *Reading and writing times: 12-hour digital clock*

This clock shows 7 hours and 35 minutes.
This is read as seven thirty-five.

1 Look at the clocks illustrated and give each of the following:
   i   The number of hours shown.
   ii The number of minutes shown.
   iii The time in words.

a    **b**

2 Write down each of these times in words:
   a 02:35   **b** 03:15   **c** 05:45   **d** 09:19   **e** 10:24   **f** 11:06

3 Show these times on a digital clock:
   a one twenty-five   **b** four forty-five   **c** six fifty-seven
   d seven twenty-three   **e** twelve five   **f** ten twenty

4 Show these times on a 24-hour digital clock:
   a thirteen twenty-five   **b** nineteen fifteen
   c twenty thirty   **d** twenty-one ten
   e twenty-three twenty   **f** twenty-two forty

5 Write down each of these times in words:
   a 13:35   **b** 21:20   **c** 20:10   **d** 20:05

6 c Reading and writing times: clocks with two hands

Many clocks have two hands: a short one to indicate the hours
and a long one to indicate the minutes. The numbers on the face
refer only to the hours, so you have to work out the minutes by
imagining the dial divided into 60 divisions, or 5 divisions
between each of the hour numbers.

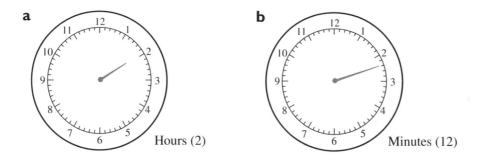

a   b

Hours (2)   Minutes (12)

Note: In **a** when the hour hand lies anywhere between the 2 and the
3 it is still indicating 2 hours. In **b** the hour numbers are multiplied
by 5 to give the number of minutes ($2 \times 5 + 2 = 12$ minutes).

Example

What time does each clock show ?

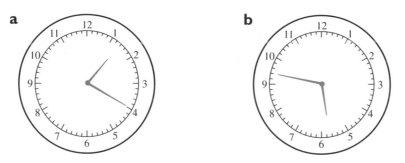

a   b

a   The hour hand points between 1 and 2, i.e. 1 hour.
    The minute hand points at the 4, i.e. $4 \times 5 = 20$ minutes.
    So the time is one twenty, or in figures 01:20.

b   The hour hand points between 5 and 6, i.e. 5 hours.
    The minute hand points at the second line past the nine,
    i.e. $9 \times 5 + 2 = 47$ minutes.
    So the time is five forty-seven, or in figures 05:47.

1 Write down the time shown on each clock.

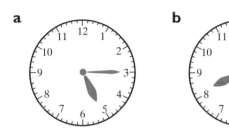

a **b** **c** **d**

2 Copy each clock and draw on the time.

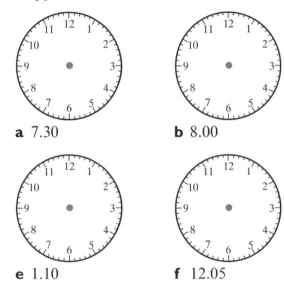

a 7.30 **b** 8.00 **c** 9.50 **d** 6.25

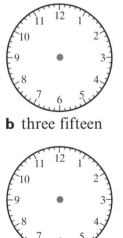

e 1.10 **f** 12.05

3 Copy each clock and draw on the time.

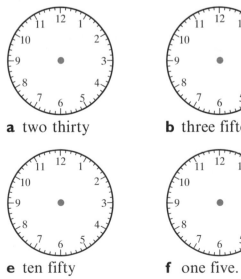

a two thirty **b** three fifteen **c** four thirty-five **d** eight twenty

e ten fifty **f** one five.

6 D *Converting between 12- and 24-hour clocks*

The day of 24 hours is split up into morning (a.m.) and afternoon (p.m.), but most clocks with hands do not show the difference. Some digital clocks can show all 24 hours, whereas others use a symbol to indicate whether the time is in the morning or afternoon.

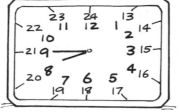

1 Do you agree that 08:10 is the same as 8.10 a.m. ?

2 Write each of these 24-hour times as an a.m. time.
  a 08:30   **b** 05:10   **c** 10:42

3 Do you agree that 9.43 a.m. is the same as 09:43 ?

4 Write each of these a.m. times as a 24-hour time.
  a 9.17 a.m.   **b** 2.52 a.m.   **c** 10.32 a.m.   **d** 11.05 a.m.

5 Do you agree that 14:10 is the same as 2.10 p.m. ? Can you get this answer by subtracting 12 from the number of hours ?

6 Write each of these 24-hour times as a p.m. time.
  a 14:30   **b** 15:10   **c** 23:42   **d** 23:55

7 Do you agree that 9.43 p.m. is the same as 21:43 ? Can you get this answer by adding 12 to the number of hours ?

8 Write each of these p.m. times as a 24-hour time.
  a 9.17 p.m.   **b** 2.52 p.m.   **c** 10.32 p.m.   **d** 11.05 p.m.

9 Show each of these times on a 24-hour digital clock:
  a 6.30 a.m.   **b** 4.50 a.m.   **c** 4.50 p.m.   **d** 11.40 p.m.

10 Write each of these 24-hour times in figures.

    a nineteen forty   **b** twenty-three twelve

    c ten thirty-four   **d** three forty-six

11 Write each of these 24-hour times in words.

    a 10:40   **b** 15:50   **c** 22:30   **d** 07:00   **e** 10:00   **f** 00:00

12 Write down the time shown as a 24-hour time.

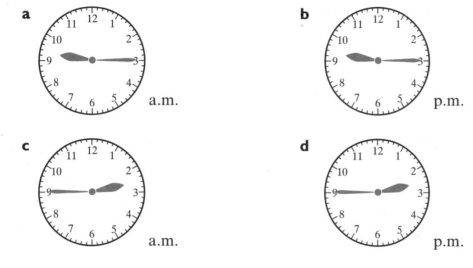

  a   a.m.   **b**   p.m.

  c   a.m.   **d**   p.m.

13 Copy and complete the table.

The first one has been done for you.

	12-hour clock	Read as	24-hour clock	Read as
a	1.30 a.m.	one thirty a.m.	01:30	one thirty
b	1.30 p.m.			
c		seven forty a.m.		
d		seven forty p.m.		
e			11:39	
f			23:39	
g				ten sixteen
h				twenty-two sixteen

6 E *Finding differences in times*

Example

  a I arrived at the football ground at 7.15 p.m. and I left the ground at 9.23 p.m. How long was I at the ground ?

  b I left home at 6.47 p.m. and I returned at 10.15 p.m. For how long was I away from home ?

  a 7.15 p.m. to 9.15 p.m. is 2 hours, 9.15 p.m. to 9.23 p.m. is 8 minutes, so 7.15 p.m. to 9.23 p.m. is 2 hours and 8 minutes.

  b 6.47 p.m. to 7.00 p.m. is 13 minutes (60 minutes in 1 hour), 7.00 p.m. to 10.00 p.m. is 3 hours, and 10.00 p.m. to 10.15 p.m. is 15 minutes, so the total time is:

13 minutes + 3 hours + 15 minutes = 3 hours 28 minutes

In **a** above it was easier to find the complete hours first and then the remaining minutes, whereas in **b** above it was better to work up to the hour and from the hour.

---

1 How long is it from:

  a 7.15 a.m. to 9.55 a.m.   **b** 4.05 p.m. to 6.35 p.m. ?

2 A film show at a cinema starts at 2.30 p.m. and ends at 5.15 p.m. How long does it last ?

3 A newspaper boy begins delivering at 5.45 a.m. and finishes at 7.15 a.m. How long did it take him to complete the round ?

4 Find the time taken by the train from London to each station.

London (Liverpool Street)	(depart)	8.05 a.m.
Bishop's Stortford	(arrive)	8.40 a.m.
Audley End	(arrive)	8.55 a.m.
Cambridge	(arrive)	9.15 a.m.
Ely	(arrive)	9.35 a.m.
King's Lynn	(arrive)	10.20 a.m.

a I arrived at the squash club at 19:03 and left at 22:22. How long was I there ?

b I arrived home from work at 18:45 and left home the next morning at 07:20. For how long was I at home ?

a 19:03 to 22:03 is 3 hours and 22:03 to 22:22 is 9 minutes, so the total time is 3 hours and 9 minutes.

b 18:45 to 19:00 is 15 minutes, 19:00 to 24:00 is 5 hours, 00:00 to 07:00 is 7 hours, and 07:00 to 07:20 is 20 minutes (15 minutes + 5 hours + 7 hours + 20 minutes), so the total time is 12 hours and 35 minutes.

Again in **a** it is easier to find the complete hours first.
However, in **b** it may be easier to find the time up to midnight and the time after midnight separately.

5 How long is it from:

   a 09:30 to 14:45   **b** 06:40 to 13:50

   c 07:20 to 16:40   **d** 05:40 to 14:10 ?

6 Find the time taken by the coach from London to Aberdeen to reach each of its five calling points.

London (Victoria Coach Station)	(depart)	08:15
Charnock Richard Service Area	(arrive)	13:20
Stirling	(arrive)	18:25
Perth	(arrive)	19:25
Dundee	(arrive)	19:55
Aberdeen	(arrive)	21:50

7 Shani arrives home at 23:10 and she watches a film which lasts until 01:25. How long does the film last ?

8 I arrived at an airport at 23:25 and had just missed a plane. The next one was not until 03:40. How long did I have to wait ?

6 F *Extracting information from cinema and TV programme guides*

Cinema programme guide for Saturday

2.30 p.m.	Doors and ticket office open
2.45 p.m.	Comic cartoon: Harry the Hedgehog
3.15 p.m.	The Burglars of Boogietown
4.30 p.m.	Journey to Mars
6.30 p.m.	Interval
6.45 p.m.	Comic cartoon: Harry the Hedgehog
7.15 p.m.	The Burglars of Boogietown
8.30 p.m.	Journey to Mars
10.30 p.m.	Cinema closes

1 How long do each of the following last ?
   a Journey to Mars   **b** The Burglars of Boogietown   **c** Harry the Hedgehog

2 For how long is the cinema open ?

3 Ayo arrived at 3.00 p.m. He liked the films so much that he
   stayed to the end of the programme.
   How long was he in the cinema ?

4 The ticket office closed at 7.45 p.m. For how long was it open ?

5 Candace arrived at 6.45 p.m. and watched all three films.
   For how long was she in the cinema ?

6 **a** Marcus arrived at 5.00 p.m. For how long was he able to watch
      the film "Journey to Mars" ?
   b Marcus decided to stay and see what he had missed of
      "Journey to Mars". What time did he leave the cinema and for
      how long was he there ?

TV programme guide

Brilliant Broadcasting Channel		Sports and Spivvies Channel	
6.00 p.m.	News and Weather	6.00 p.m.	News and Weather
6.20 p.m.	Local News	6.30 p.m.	Football:
6.30 p.m.	The Jones Family		Liverpool v Arsenal
7.15 p.m.	Film: Cowboy Charlie of California	8.25 p.m.	Comedy: Hopeless Harry and
9.00 p.m.	News and Weather		Moaning Minnie
9.30 p.m.	Documentary:	9.45 p.m.	Hockey:
	The Large Lizards of Loonieland		Stafford v Leicester
10.15 p.m.	Film: Gangster Gregory of	10.30 p.m.	Film: Sam the Saver and
	Greedytown		Winnie the Waster
11.55 p.m.	Late-night News	11.55 p.m.	News and Weather
12.00 p.m.	Closedown	12.00 p.m.	Closedown

7 For how long do each of the following last ?
  a Sam the Saver and Winnie the Waster
  b Hopeless Harry and Moaning Minnie
  c Cowboy Charlie of California
  d Football programme

8 Three programmes (other than News) last for the same time.
   Which three programmes are these and for how long do they last ?

9 Josiah wants to watch the football programme, but he wants to
   see the whole of the film "Cowboy Charlie of California". If he
   has no video recorder, how long can he watch the football
   programme for ?

l The dentists' timetable for Tuesday morning is shown below.

Time	Mr. Simpson (check-ups)	Mr. Fletcher (ordinary surgery)	Miss Patel (anaesthetic surgery)
9.00 a.m.	Mr. Jones	Mrs. Powell	Miss Nouihed
9.15 a.m.	Miss Carr		Mr. Mitchell
9.30 a.m.	Miss Khan	Mrs. Bailey	Mr. Mitchell
9.45 a.m.		Miss Johnson	Mrs. Udoma
10.00 a.m.			Mr. Mistry
10.15 a.m.	Mr. Rathod	Mr. Brown	Miss Singh
10.30 a.m.	Mrs. Read	Mr. Thuo	

a At what time, with whom and for what purpose do each of the
   following have an appointment ?
   i Miss Carr   **ii** Mrs. Read   **iii** Miss Nouihed   **iv** Mr. Rathod
b Who is seeing:
   i Mr. Simpson at 9.00 a.m.
   ii Mr. Fletcher at 10.15 a.m.
   iii Miss Patel at 9.45 a.m. ?
c When is the earliest free appointment and with which dentist ?
d Unfortunately there was an accident nearby at 10.15 a.m. and
   two emergency cases had to be dealt with, one required
   ordinary surgery and the other required anaesthetic surgery.
   Which two patients have to wait to be treated ?
e Miss Khan arrived exactly on time for her appointment but
   waited to take Miss Singh home after her anaesthetic surgery.
   If Miss Singh's appointment last for 15 minutes, for how long
   was Miss Khan at the surgery ?

2 The Wonderful Wensleydale Railway Company has reopened the railway from Northallerton to Garsdale. The timetable is shown below.

Westbound:				
Northallerton	10:15	12:25	14:35	16:50
Bedale	10:45	12:55	15:05	17:20
Leyburn	11:15	13:25	15:35	17:50
Aysgarth	11:40	13:50	16:00	18:15
Hawes	12:05	14:15	16:25	18:40
Garsdale	12:15	14:25	16:35	18:50
Eastbound:				
Garsdale	10:15	12:25	14:35	16:50
Hawes	10:25			
Aysgarth	10:50			
Leyburn	11:15			
Bedale	11:45			
Northallerton	12:15			

a If all trains take the same time between all stations, copy and complete the Eastbound timetable.

b A group of people want to go from Northallerton to Garsdale for an afternoon hike.
What is the longest time they can have at Garsdale ?

c Mrs. Garthwaite wants to go from Hawes to Northallerton to visit a friend. If she cannot leave until early afternoon, what is the longest time she can have in Northallerton ?

d Mr. Rutterford has to go from Hawes to Bedale to see his business partner. He has to make the journey as early as possible and return as soon as possible.
How much time will he have in Bedale ?

7 Calendars

7 A Idea of years, months, weeks and days

JANUARY 2000						
M	T	W	TH	F	S	S
					1	2
3	4	5	6	7	8	9
10	11	12	13	14	15	16
17	18	19	20	21	22	23
24	25	26	27	28	29	30
31						

FEBRUARY 2000						
M	T	W	TH	F	S	S
	1	2	3	4	5	6
7	8	9	10	11	12	13
14	15	16	17	18	19	20
21	22	23	24	25	26	27
28	29					

1 How many days are there in January 2000 ?

2 How many days are there in February 2000 ?

3 How many days are there in one week ?

4 How many days are there in a normal year ?

5 How many complete weeks are there in a year ?

6 Look at the calendar for January 2000 above.
Write down the day of the week which is:
  a 1 January   **b** 5 January   **c** 13 January   **d** 29 January.

7 On which day in January 2000 is:
  a the first Monday   **b** the second Thursday
  c the fourth Wednesday   **d** the fifth Sunday ?

8 Look at the calendar for February 2000 above.
Write down the day of the week which is:
  a 3 February   **b** 8 February
  c 17 February   **d** 28 February.

9 On which day in February 2000 is:
  a the second Saturday   **b** the third Thursday
  c the first Wednesday   **d** the fourth Friday ?

7 B   *Converting between weeks and days*

1 January has 31 days. Which other months also have 31 days ?

2 April has 30 days. Which other months also have 30 days ?

3 There are 28 days in February in a normal year.
How many days are there in February in a leap year ?

4 There are 7 days in one week. How many days are there in:
   a 2 weeks   **b** 10 weeks ?

5 How many weeks are there in:
   a 28 days   **b** 77 days ?

6 There are 12 months in one year. How many months are there in:
   a 2 years   **b** 12 years ?

7 How many years are there in:
   a 48 months   **b** 96 months ?

8 There are 365 days in a normal year.
How many days are there in a leap year ?

9 How often do we get a leap year ?

10 How many Mondays will there be in the year 2000 ?

11 There are 52 complete weeks in 1 year.
How many complete weeks are there in:
   a 2 years   **b** 15 years ?

12 How many complete years are there in:
   a 105 weeks   **b** 365 weeks ?

7 c *Finding differences in time between dates*

There are four days from 5 February to 9 February.

I Find how many days there are from the first date to the second date.

   a 3 January to 9 January

   b 7 March to 13 March

   c 17 May to 31 May

   d 11 July to 6 August

Example

Suppose today is Friday 16 October. Find each of the following:

   a the date last Friday   **b** the date next Friday

   c the date in two weeks' time   **d** the day and date in 10 days' time.

a $16 - 7 = 9$ so last Friday was the 9 October.

b $16 + 7 = 23$ so next Friday will be the 23 October.

c $16 + 7 + 7 = 30$ so in two weeks time it will be Friday 30 October.

d $16 + 10 = 26$ so the date will be 26 October.

As $10 = 7 + 3$ the day will be 3 days after next Friday and will therefore be a Monday. In 10 days' time it will be Monday 26 October.

---

2 Today is Saturday the 10th of March. Find each of the following:

   a the date last Saturday   **b** the date next Saturday

   c the date in two weeks' time   **d** the day and date in nine days' time.

3 Today is Sunday the 13th of August. Find each of the following:

   a the date last Sunday   **b** the date next Sunday

   c the date in two weeks' time   **d** the day and date in 10 days' time.

4 Find how many days there are from the first date up to and including the second date.

   a 17 March to 6 April

   b 21 May to 10 July

   c 17 October to 14 December

   d 31 January to 1 December

Example _____

If today is Monday 4 July, find each of the following:

a the date this coming Wednesday

b the date on Wednesday next week

c the day and date in 22 days' time.

a $4 + 2 = 6$ so the date on this coming Wednesday is 6 July.

b $4 + 7 + 2 = 13$ so the date on Wednesday next week is 13 July.

c $4 + 22 = 26$ so the date will be 26 July. As $22 = 3 \times 7 + 1$ the day will be one day after a Monday, i.e. a Tuesday, so it will be Tuesday 26 July.

_____

5 Today is Monday the 7th of July. Find each of the following:

   a the date this coming Thursday

   b the date on Thursday next week

   c the day and date in 17 days' time

   d the day and date in 23 days' time.

6 Today is Wednesday the 2nd of February. Find:

   a the date this coming Friday

   b the date on each subsequent Friday for the rest of the month

   c the day and date in 15 days' time

   d the day and date in 27 days' time, given that this year is a leap year.

Example

Part of a calendar is shown in each of parts **a** and **b** below.

(They are not for the same month.)

Complete the rest of the dates for Tuesdays and Wednesdays in these two months.

a

Tuesday					
Wednesday			12	19	

b

Tuesday			16	
Wednesday				31

c

Tuesday	4	11	18	25	
Wednesday		5	12	19	26

d

Tuesday	2	9	16	23	30
Wednesday	3	10	17	24	31

1 Part of a calendar is shown in each part of the question below.
Each calendar is a different 31-day month. Copy and complete
the rest of the dates for each case.

a

Saturday			24	
Sunday	4			

b

Monday				28
Tuesday		15		

c

Wednesday			24	
Thursday				
Friday		12		

d

Wednesday	7			
Thursday				
Friday				30

For questions **2** to **6** copy the calendars for January and February below.

1998						
January	Monday		5	12	19	26
	Tuesday		6	13	20	27
	Wednesday		7	14	21	28
	Thursday	1	8	15	22	29
	Friday	2	9	16	23	30
	Saturday	3	10	17	24	31
	Sunday	4	11	18	25	

1998						
February	Monday		2	9	16	23
	Tuesday		3	10	17	24
	Wednesday		4	11	18	25
	Thursday		5	12	19	26
	Friday		6	13	20	27
	Saturday		7	14	21	28
	Sunday	1	8	15	22	

2 Write down the day of the week for each of the following dates:

   a 1 January   **b** 5 January   **c** 10 January   **d** 21 January

3 On which date in January is each of the following:

   a the first Monday   **b** the second Tuesday

   c the third Monday   **d** the fourth Friday ?

4 Write down the day of the week for each of the following dates:

   a February 3rd   **b** February 6th   **c** February 18th   **d** February 21st.

5 On which date in February is each of the following:

   a the first Wednesday   **b** the second Monday

   c the third Tuesday   **d** the fourth Sunday ?

6 a On what day of the week will the 1st of March fall ?

   b Make out a calendar for March 1998.

7 What will be the date in March on:

   a the first Wednesday   **b** the first Sunday

   c the third Wednesday   **d** the third Thursday ?

8 Which days occur five times in March and what is the date on the fifth occurrence of each of these days ?

COPY ⊘   105

8 Decimals

8 A *Idea of decimal, ordering and place value*

In the number line below, each of the whole numbers has been divided
into ten equal divisions. We use the decimal 4.3 to represent the point A.

1 Do you agree that the point B is represented by the decimal 1.8 ?

2 Look at the number line above.
Write down the decimal that represents each of these points:

   a C   **b** D   **c** E   **d** F   **e** G   **f** H   **g** I   **h** J

3 On a copy of the number line below draw an arrow to represent
each of the following decimals.

   A 1.3   B 2.1   C 3.4   D 4.5   E 6.8   F 9.6   G 5.9   H 9.0   I 0.7

4 a Which is the largest of these decimals: 3.4, 1.8, 5.1, 2.9, 4.5 ?

   b Write the five decimals in part **a** in order, starting with the largest.

Example

We can use the column headings
of Tens, Units and Tenths to
denote the place value of each
figure in a number such as 24.3:

Tens	Units		Tenths
2	4	.	3

The place value of the 2 is two tens, or 20
The place value of the 4 is four units, or 4
The place value of the 3 is three tenths, or 0.3 $\left(\text{or } \frac{3}{10}\right)$

5 Write down the place value of the underlined figure:

   a 2<u>4</u>.7   **b** 45.<u>2</u>   **c** 62.<u>9</u>   **d** <u>4</u>2.3   **e** 54.<u>8</u>   **f** 26.<u>1</u>

Example

If we wanted to show a point between 2.10 and 2.20 (i.e. between 2.1 and 2.2) on a number line we could divide the gap between them into ten further divisions. The point A is six of these divisions to the right of 2.1. We therefore use the decimal 2.16 to represent this point.

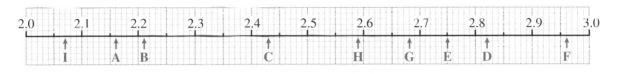

6 Look at the number line above. Write down the decimal that represents the point:

    a B   **b** C   **c** D   **d** E   **e** F   **f** G   **g** H   **h** I

7 On a copy of the number line below draw an arrow to represent each of the following decimals.

    a 4.13   **b** 4.24   **c** 4.52   **d** 4.71   **e** 4.65   **f** 4.37   **g** 4.46   **h** 4.8

```
4.0      4.1      4.2      4.3      4.4      4.5      4.6      4.7      4.8      4.9      5.0
```

8 a Which is the smallest of these decimals: 4.99, 7.32, 2.65, 5.71 ?

  b Write the four decimals in part **a** in order, starting with the smallest.

Example

We can use the column headings of Tens, Units, Tenths and Hundredths to denote the place value of each figure in a number such as 42.57:

Tens	Units		Tenths	Hundredths
4	2	.	5	7

The place value of the 4 is four tens or 40

The place value of the 2 is two units or 2

The place value of the 5 is five tenths or 0.5 $\left(\text{or } \frac{5}{10}\right)$

The place value of the 7 is seven hundredths or 0.07 $\left(\text{or } \frac{7}{100}\right)$

9 Write down the place value of the underlined figure:

    a 4_2_.71   **b** 54.2_8_   **c** 2_6_.91   **d** 14.2_3_   **e** 35._4_8   **f** _5_2.61

I Press the following buttons on your calculator:

[AC] [1] [.] [2] [+] [4] [.] [5] [=]

Did you get the answer 5.7 ? What is 1.2 + 4.5 ?

2 Use your calculator to find:

   a 2.3 + 1.6   **b** 3.5 + 4.3   **c** 7.3 + 4.9   **d** 8.7 + 9.6

3 Use your calculator to find:

   a 23.1 + 16.9   **b** 35.4 + 43.6   **c** 73.45 + 49.83   **d** 24.26 + 16.81

4 Press the following buttons on your calculator:

[AC] [4] [.] [5] [−] [1] [.] [2] [=]

Did you get the answer 3.3 ? What is 4.5 − 1.2 ?

5 Use your calculator to find:

   a 2.8 − 1.6   **b** 6.5 − 4.3   **c** 7.3 − 4.9   **d** 8.1 − 3.7

6 Use your calculator to find:

   a 23.1 − 11.1   **b** 45.4 − 33.4   **c** 35.29 − 17.46   **d** 39 − 11.57

7 The handle of a screwdriver is 6.4 cm long and the projecting
length of the blade is 7.9 cm. Find the overall length.

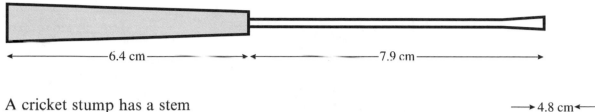

8 A cricket stump has a stem
of length 65.6 cm and a
point of length 4.8 cm.
Find the overall length.

9 John is 1.57 metres tall. If he stands on a stool which is
0.35 metres tall, how high does he stand above the floor ?

10 Find the thickness of the washer ring.

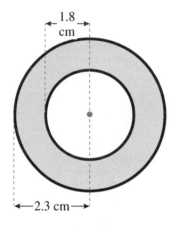

11 It is 8.5 miles from Hemel Hempstead to Watford. I am given a
lift from Hemel Hempstead to Hunton Bridge which is a distance
of 6.6 miles. If I walk the rest of the way, how far do I walk ?

12 The total depth of a swimming pool is 1.60 metres,
but the water level is 0.25 cm below the edge.
What is the depth of the water ?

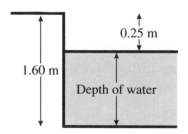

8 c   *Multiplication and division of decimals (with a calculator)*

1 Press the following buttons on your calculator:

$\boxed{\text{AC}}\ \boxed{1}\ \boxed{.}\ \boxed{2}\ \boxed{\times}\ \boxed{3}\ \boxed{=}$

Did you get the answer 3.6 ? What is 1.2×3 ?

2 Use your calculator to find:

    a 2.3×3 **b** 7.3×51 **c** 4.2×16 **d** 7.5×24

3 Use your calculator to find:

    a 23.5×3 **b** 51.5×5 **c** 42.5×29 **d** 51.6×15

4 Press the following buttons on your calculator:

$\boxed{\text{AC}}\ \boxed{3}\ \boxed{6}\ \boxed{.}\ \boxed{9}\ \boxed{\div}\ \boxed{3}\ \boxed{=}$

Did you get the answer 12.3 ? What is $36.9 \div 3$?

5 Use your calculator to find:

    a $84.3 \div 3$ **b** $51.6 \div 4$ **c** $72.6 \div 66$ **d** $80 \div 32$

6 Use your calculator to find:

    a $2.43 \div 3$ **b** $3.16 \div 4$ **c** $6.72 \div 24$ **d** $4.92 \div 12$

7 A piece of wood 3.2 m long is sawn into 5 equal lengths. How long will each piece be ?

8 How high will a pile of 12 books be if each is 1.8 cm thick ?

9 A supermarket sells milk in large plastic containers of mass 2.3 kilograms. Find the mass of 6 of these containers.

10 If the distance between each pair of places shown is 12.5 miles, find the distance from Stratford to Woodstock.

Stratford
Shipston
Chipping Norton
Woodstock

11 A viaduct is 122.5 m long and has 5 equal arches. What is the length of each arch ?

←?→
122.5 m

12 Ayo has a portable TV with a screen of width 14.5 cm. The large TV in his living room, however, has a screen 4 times wider. Find the width of the screen on his large TV.

13 A gate of width 1.08 m is made from 6 boards of wood of equal width. Find the width of each board.

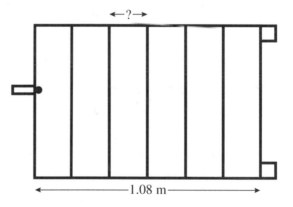

←?→
1.08 m

14 5 wholesale bags of sugar are on the platform of a large weighing machine. If the dial reads 252.5 kg, what is the weight of each bag ?

15 A motorway is 67.5 miles long. If the junctions shown are equally spaced, what is the distance between the two service areas ?

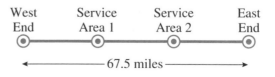

West End   Service Area 1   Service Area 2   East End
← 67.5 miles →

9 Fractions

9 A Idea of fractions: halves and quarters

The simplest kind of fraction refers to one part of a whole quantity. Look at the circles below.

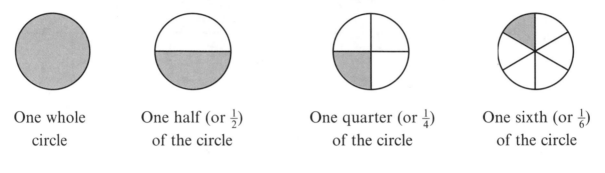

| One whole circle | One half (or $\frac{1}{2}$) of the circle | One quarter (or $\frac{1}{4}$) of the circle | One sixth (or $\frac{1}{6}$) of the circle |

1 State in words and write as a fraction the part of the diagram which is shaded.

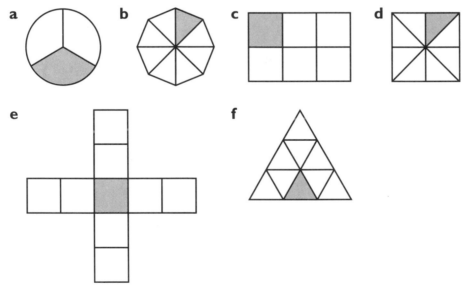

a   b   c   d

e   f

2 Copy the diagram and illustrate the fraction given by shading.

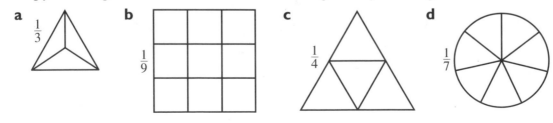

a $\frac{1}{3}$ b $\frac{1}{9}$ c $\frac{1}{4}$ d $\frac{1}{7}$

Fractions can also refer to more than one part of a whole quantity.
Look at the rectangles below.

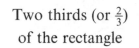

| One whole rectangle | Three quarters (or $\frac{3}{4}$) of the rectangle | Two thirds (or $\frac{2}{3}$) of the rectangle | Five sixths (or $\frac{5}{6}$) of the rectangle |

3 State in words and write as a fraction the part of the diagram
which is shaded.

a

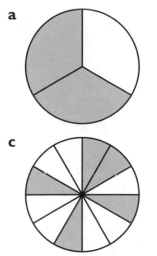

b

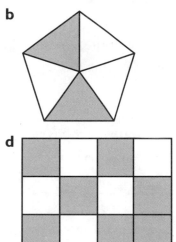

c

d

4 Copy the diagram and illustrate the fraction given by shading.

a

$\frac{3}{8}$

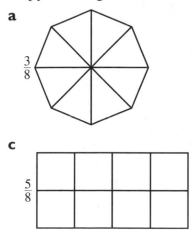

b

$\frac{4}{5}$

c

$\frac{5}{8}$

d

$\frac{7}{10}$

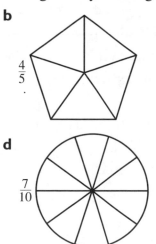

9 B   *Finding halves and quarters of quantities*

Example

Hitesh has saved £36.
He spends half of his savings on a small radio.
How much does the radio cost ?
His radio costs:
$\frac{1}{2}$ of £36 = £36 ÷ 2 = £18

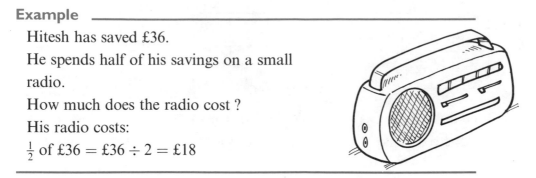

1 There are 26 members in the local youth club. Half the members cycle to the club. How many members cycle to the club meetings ?

2 Sandra earns £64 working in the supermarket at the weekends. Each week she saves half of this money. How much does she save ?

3 There are 450 members in the local leisure club. Half of the members are male. How many of the members are female ?

Example

Janie has £28.
She spends one quarter of this on a new CD.
How much does the CD cost ?

The CD costs $\frac{1}{4}$ of £28 = £28 ÷ 4 = £7

4 There are 32 people in an evening class. One quarter of these are female. How many females are there in the evening class ?

5 Andy's uncle gives him £60 for his birthday. Andy decides to spend one quarter of this on a torch.
  a How much does the torch cost ?
  b How much of the £60 does he have left ?

6 Anit goes on a two-week holiday with £360. After one week he has half of his money left and at the end of the holiday he has one quarter left. Find how much he has left:
   a after one week   **b** at the end of his holiday.

7 The distance from London to Leeds is 304 km.
Find the distance from London to:
   a Leicester, if it is half as far
   b Bedford, if it is one quarter as far.

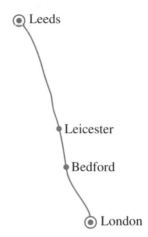

8 Mr. Gray's weight is 76 kg. Find the weight of:
   a his son James, if he is half as heavy
   b his daughter Jean, if she is one quarter as heavy.

9 A supermarket sells milk in four-pint containers, but they are actually marked "2272 millilitres".
Find the number of millilitres in:
   a a two-pint container   **b** a one-pint container.

10 a A bus journey for the 42 miles from Darlington to Hawes takes 2 hours 24 minutes (144 minutes).
     Find the time taken from Darlington to:
     i Leyburn, if it is half as long
     ii Richmond, if it is one quarter as long.
   b Find the distance from Darlington to Richmond, if it is one third as far.

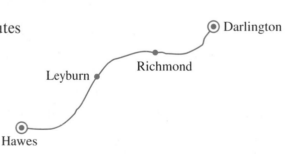

10 Temperature

10 A *Idea of temperature and negative numbers*

When measuring temperatures we usually describe temperatures above the freezing point of 0°C as positive, and temperatures below the freezing point as negative.

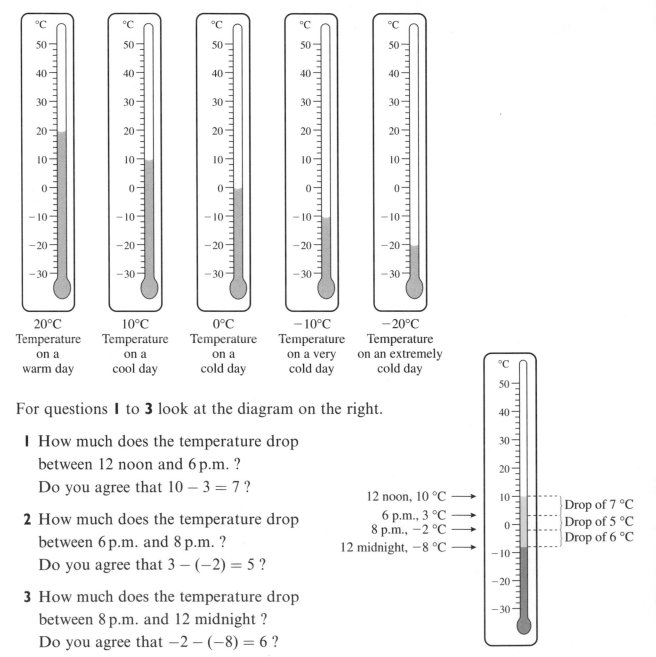

20°C	10°C	0°C	−10°C	−20°C
Temperature on a warm day	Temperature on a cool day	Temperature on a cold day	Temperature on a very cold day	Temperature on an extremely cold day

For questions **1** to **3** look at the diagram on the right.

1 How much does the temperature drop between 12 noon and 6 p.m. ?
   Do you agree that $10 - 3 = 7$?

2 How much does the temperature drop between 6 p.m. and 8 p.m. ?
   Do you agree that $3 - (-2) = 5$?

3 How much does the temperature drop between 8 p.m. and 12 midnight ?
   Do you agree that $-2 - (-8) = 6$?

12 noon, 10 °C ⟶
6 p.m., 3 °C ⟶
8 p.m., −2 °C ⟶
12 midnight, −8 °C ⟶

Drop of 7 °C
Drop of 5 °C
Drop of 6 °C

4 The table below shows how the temperature dropped between 12 noon and 6 p.m. on five days during a certain week in April. Copy and complete the table.

Day	Temperature at 12 noon	Drop in temperature	Temperature at 6 p.m.
Monday	15°C	5°C	
Tuesday	17°C	6°C	
Wednesday	13°C	8°C	
Thursday	12°C	9°C	
Friday	11°C	7°C	

5 The table below shows how the temperature dropped between 12 noon, 6 p.m. and 12 midnight on five days during a certain week in December. Copy and complete the table.

Day	Temperature at 12 noon	Drop in temperature	Temperature at 6 p.m.	Drop in temperature	Temperature at 12 midnight
Monday	5°C	7°C		6°C	
Tuesday	4°C	7°C		3°C	
Wednesday	6°C	7°C		3°C	
Thursday	4°C	9°C		3°C	
Friday	3°C	9°C		1°C	

6 The table below shows how the temperature rose between 6 a.m. and 12 noon on five days during a certain week in January. Copy and complete the table.

Day	Temperature at 6 a.m.	Rise in temperature	Temperature at 12 noon
Monday	−4°C	6°C	
Tuesday	−5°C	6°C	
Wednesday	−7°C	9°C	
Thursday	−6°C	8°C	
Friday	−6°C	7°C	

10 B *Calculating temperature differences*

1 The temperature at 12 noon one day is 5°C, but by 6 p.m. it has dropped to −1°C, and by 9 p.m. it has dropped to −6°C.
Find the drop in temperature between:
a 12 noon and 6 p.m.　　**b** 6 p.m. and 9 p.m.

2 The table below shows how the temperature dropped between 12 noon and 6 p.m. and between 6 p.m. and 12 midnight on each day during a certain week in February. Copy and complete the table.

Day	Temperature at 12 noon	Drop in temperature	Temperature at 6 p.m.	Drop in temperature	Temperature at 12 midnight
Monday	5°C		−3°C		−7°C
Tuesday	6°C		−4°C		−9°C
Wednesday	7°C		−2°C		−5°C
Thursday	6°C		−5°C		−7°C
Friday	8°C		−2°C		−6°C
Saturday	4°C		−3°C		−8°C
Sunday	5°C		−2°C		−7°C

3 The table below shows how the temperature varied between early morning, lunch time and tea time on each day of a certain week in February. Copy and complete the table.

Day	Temperature at 6 a.m.	Rise during the morning	Temperature at 12 noon	Fall during the afternoon	Temperature at 6 p.m.	Net rise between 6 a.m. and 6 p.m.
Monday	−5°C		7°C		−3°C	
Tuesday	−4°C		9°C		−2°C	
Wednesday	−3°C		8°C		−1°C	
Thursday	−6°C		4°C		−2°C	
Friday	−2°C		10°C		4°C	
Saturday	−1°C		11°C		3°C	
Sunday	−3°C		9°C		1°C	

  COPY✓

4 The table below shows how the temperature varied between early morning, lunch time and tea time on each day during a certain week in January. Copy and complete the table.

Day	Temperature at 6 a.m.	Rise during the morning	Temperature at 12 noon	Fall during the afternoon	Temperature at 6 p.m.	Net rise between 6 a.m. and 6 p.m.
Monday	−6°C	11°C		7°C		
Tuesday	−5°C	13°C		11°C		
Wednesday	−4°C	10°C		7°C		
Thursday	−3°C	13°C		12°C		
Friday	−2°C	11°C		6°C		
Saturday	−3°C	10°C		5°C		
Sunday	−1°C	9°C		7°C		

5 The table below shows how the temperature varied between early morning, lunch time and tea time on each day during a certain week in March. Copy and complete the table.

Day	Temperature at 6 a.m.	Rise during the morning	Temperature at 12 noon	Fall during the afternoon	Temperature at 6 p.m.	Net fall between 6 a.m. and 6 p.m.
Monday	−3°C	5°C		7°C		
Tuesday	−1°C	6°C		9°C		
Wednesday	−2°C	8°C		10°C		
Thursday	1°C	6°C		9°C		
Friday	3°C	5°C		10°C		
Saturday	2°C	3°C		8°C		
Sunday	1°C	4°C		10°C		

11 Length

11 A *Idea of length: language, comparison and order*

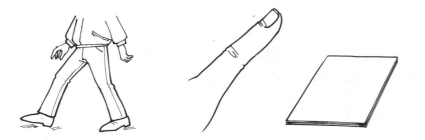

The main units of length are the metre, the centimetre and the millimetre.

One metre (m) is about the length of a man's full stride.

One centimetre (cm) is about the width of a man's little finger nail.

There are 100 centimetres in 1 metre: 1 m = 100 cm.

One millimetre is about the thickness of 10 sheets of paper in a pile.

There are 10 millimetres in 1 centimetre: 1 cm = 10 mm.

1 Do you agree that the height of a door is about 2 metres ?

2 Is the width of a door more or less than one metre ?

3 Estimate in metres how long and how wide your table is.

4 Estimate in metres how long and how wide your room is.

5 Which of the two lines is the longer ?

6 Which of the two lines is the shorter ?

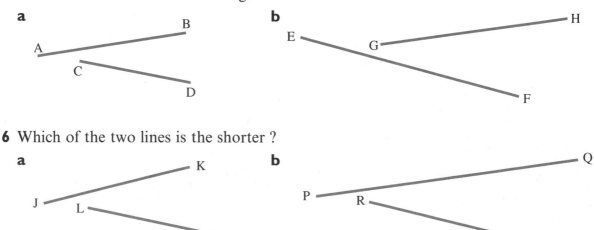

7 Look at the lines drawn on the right.

   a Which is the longest line ?

   b Which is the shortest line ?

   c Put the lines in order, longest first.

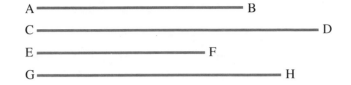

8 The lines AB, CD, EF and XY are drawn on a grid of 1 cm squares.

   a Do you agree that the length of AB is 3 cm ?

   b Write down the length of:

   i CD   **ii** EF   **iii** XY

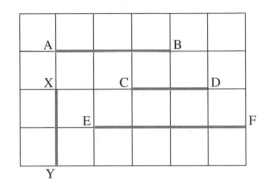

9 These lines are drawn on a grid of 1 cm squares. Write down the length of each line.

   a AB =

   b CD =

   c EF =

   d GH =

   e KL =

   f MN =

   g PQ =

   h RS =

   i TU =

   j VW =

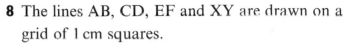

11 B *Using a ruler to measure lengths in centimetres and millimetres*

1 Use the centimetre ruler to say how long each line is.

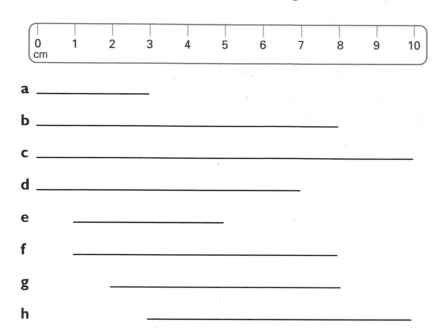

a ——————

b ————————————————

c ——————————————————————

d ——————————————————

e   ——————————

f   ————————————————

g   ————————————

h   ——————————————

2 Use the centimetre and millimetre ruler to say how long each line is.

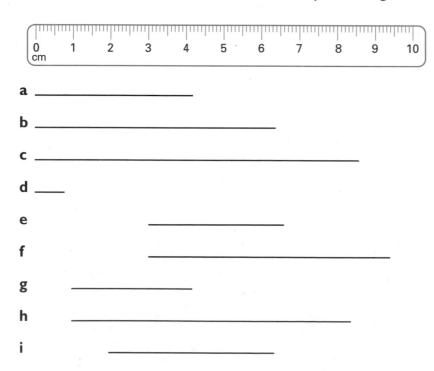

a ——————————

b ——————————————

c ——————————————————

d ——

e   ————————

f   ——————————————

g   ————————

h   ——————————————

i   ——————————

Example

Write down the length of:

a the handle   **b** the shaft   **c** the whole screwdriver.

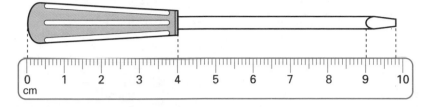

a The handle is 4 cm long.

b The shaft is (9 − 4) cm or 5 cm long.

c The overall length of the screwdriver is 9 cm 8 mm.

Note: The handle has to be aligned with the zero mark and not with the end of the ruler.

---

3 Write down the length of the needle.

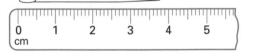

4 Write down the length of the pin.

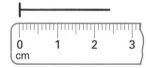

5 Write down the length of the hinge.

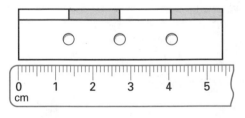

6 Write down the length of the tweezers.

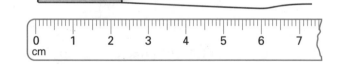

7 Write down:

    a the overall length of the dart   **b** the length of the flight

    c the length of the stem   **d** the length of the pointed end.

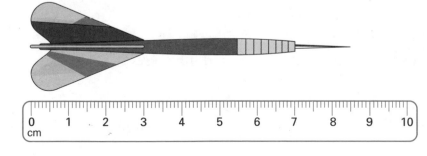

11 c *Drawing lines of given lengths*

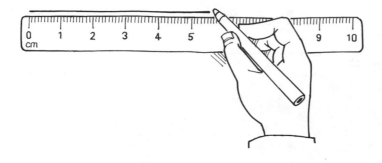

When drawing a line it is important to align the 0 mark on the ruler with the beginning of the line.

1 Use a centimetre ruler to draw a line of the given length.

```
0    1    2    3    4    5    6    7    8    9    10
cm
```

a 3 cm   **b** 7 cm   **c** 9 cm   **d** 6 cm

2 Use a centimetre/millimetre ruler to draw a line of the given length.

```
0    1    2    3    4    5    6    7    8    9    10
cm
```

a 3 cm 2 mm   **b** 7 cm 4 mm   **c** 4 cm 5 mm   **d** 9 cm 1 mm

3 Use a centimetre/millimetre ruler to draw each line to the given length.

  a AB: 2 cm   **b** CD: 2 cm 5 mm
  c EF: 6 cm   **d** GH: 6 cm 1 mm
  e JK: 5 cm   **f** LM: 5 cm 3 mm
  g NP: 8 cm   **h** QR: 8 cm 4 mm

4 Use a metre rule to mark out on the floor a length of:
  a 2 metres   **b** 3 metres   **c** 5 metres   **d** 10 metres

5 Use a metre rule to mark out a length of:
  a 60 cm   **b** 80 cm   **c** 1 m 20 cm   **d** 1 m 90 cm

11 D *Converting between millimetres, centimetres and metres*

1 a Do you agree that there are 10 millimetres in 1 centimetre ?
  b Copy and complete the statement: $1\,cm = $ _____ mm.

2 How many millimetres are there in:
  a 2 cm   **b** 5 cm ?

3 How many centimetres are there in:
  a 40 mm   **b** 60 mm   **c** 70 mm   **d** 100 mm ?

4 a Do you agree that there are 100 centimetres in 1 metre ?
  b Copy and complete the statement: $1\,m = $ _____ cm.

5 How many centimetres are there in:
  a 2 m   **b** 5 m ?

6 How many centimetres are there in:
  a 1 m and 20 cm   **b** 1 m and 59 cm   **c** 2 m and 30 cm
  d 3 m and 40 cm   **e** 5 m and 50 cm   **f** 6 m and 9 cm ?

7 How many metres are there in:
  a 400 cm   **b** 600 cm   **c** 800 cm   **d** 1000 cm ?

8 How many metres and centimetres are there in:
  a 120 cm   **b** 154 cm   **c** 230 cm   **d** 236 cm   **e** 378 cm   **f** 609 cm ?

Example _____

  1.23 m means 1 m and 23 cm
  2.07 m means 2 m and 7 cm

_____

9 Write the number of metres and centimetres in:
  a 143 cm   **b** 185 cm   **c** 196 cm   **d** 261 cm   **e** 372 cm   **f** 103 cm

10 Write as metres:
  a 153 cm   **b** 191 cm   **c** 138 cm   **d** 236 cm   **e** 374 cm   **f** 604 cm

11 Write as centimetres:
  a 1.97 m   **b** 1.25 m   **c** 2.64 m   **d** 5.57 m   **e** 9.38 m   **f** 1.08 m

11 E   *Addition and subtraction of lengths*

The perimeter of a shape is the total distance around the outside of the shape.

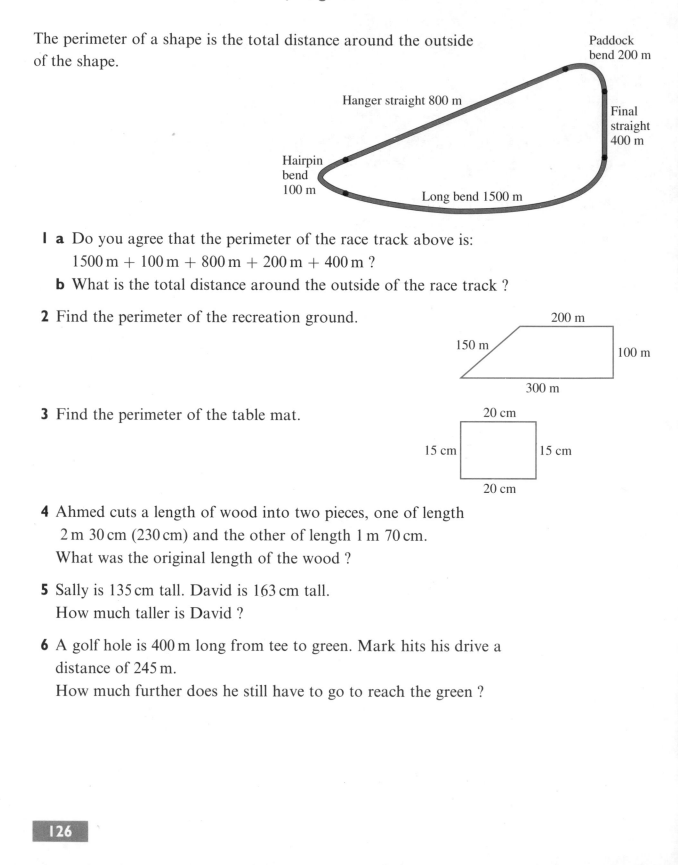

1 a Do you agree that the perimeter of the race track above is:
   1500 m + 100 m + 800 m + 200 m + 400 m ?
  b What is the total distance around the outside of the race track ?

2 Find the perimeter of the recreation ground.

3 Find the perimeter of the table mat.

4 Ahmed cuts a length of wood into two pieces, one of length
   2 m 30 cm (230 cm) and the other of length 1 m 70 cm.
   What was the original length of the wood ?

5 Sally is 135 cm tall. David is 163 cm tall.
   How much taller is David ?

6 A golf hole is 400 m long from tee to green. Mark hits his drive a
   distance of 245 m.
   How much further does he still have to go to reach the green ?

Example

Find: $1.73\,\text{m} + 2.38\,\text{m}$

We can show this as:

	m	cm	
	1	73	i.e. 1.73 m
+	2	38	i.e. 2.38 m
	4	11	i.e. 4.11 m

So $1.73\,\text{m} + 2.38\,\text{m} = 4.11\,\text{m}$

---

7 Find:

   a $1.25\,\text{m} + 1.50\,\text{m}$ **b** $3.52\,\text{m} + 1.24\,\text{m}$

8 Add together:

   a $1.12\,\text{m}$ and $3.69\,\text{m}$ **b** $5.16\,\text{m}$ and $0.39\,\text{m}$

9 Find the sum of:

   a $2.84\,\text{m}$ and $6.59\,\text{m}$ **b** $3.63\,\text{m}$ and $5.89\,\text{m}$

10 Don's car is 4.47 m long. His caravan is 6.35 m long.
What is the total length when he is towing his caravan ?

Example

Find: $3.38\,\text{m} - 2.13\,\text{m}$

We can show this as:

	m	cm	
	3	38	i.e. 3.38 m
+	2	13	i.e. 2.13 m
	1	25	i.e. 1.25 m

So $3.38\,\text{m} - 2.13\,\text{m} = 1.25\,\text{m}$

---

11 Find:

   a $3.75\,\text{m} - 1.50\,\text{m}$ **b** $5.69\,\text{m} - 2.23\,\text{m}$

12 Find the difference between:

   a $3.61\,\text{m}$ and $1.12\,\text{m}$ **b** $6.29\,\text{m}$ and $0.96\,\text{m}$

13 Subtract:

   a $2.91\,\text{m}$ from $6.59\,\text{m}$ **b** $2.48\,\text{m}$ from $3.13\,\text{m}$

14 Mark is 1.63 m tall. Ian is 1.48 m tall. How much shorter is Ian ?

1 A rubber band is 9 cm long.
   If it is stretched by 7 cm, how long is it now ?

2 Find the total length of the cricket bat.

3 How far does John have to walk
   when he goes to school ?

4 The two hands of a clock are of length 6 cm and 4 cm.
   What is the distance between the ends of the hands at
   a 6 o'clock   **b** 12 o'clock ?

5 Josiah has a tent peg of length 20 cm. He hammers it a distance
   of 12 cm into the ground.
   How high does the tent peg project above the ground ?

6 A screwdriver is 25 cm long.
   If the projecting length of the blade is 12 cm,
   how long is the handle ?

7 How far is it from the post office to
   Meg's school ?

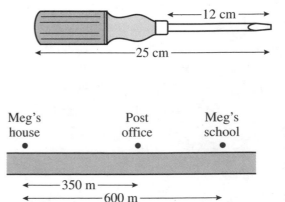

8 My car has a length of 3 m 90 cm and I am towing a trailer of length 2 m 60 cm. What is the total length of both vehicles ?

9 Find the total length of the engineer's plumbline if the cord has a length of 1 m 39 cm and the bob has a length of 11 cm.

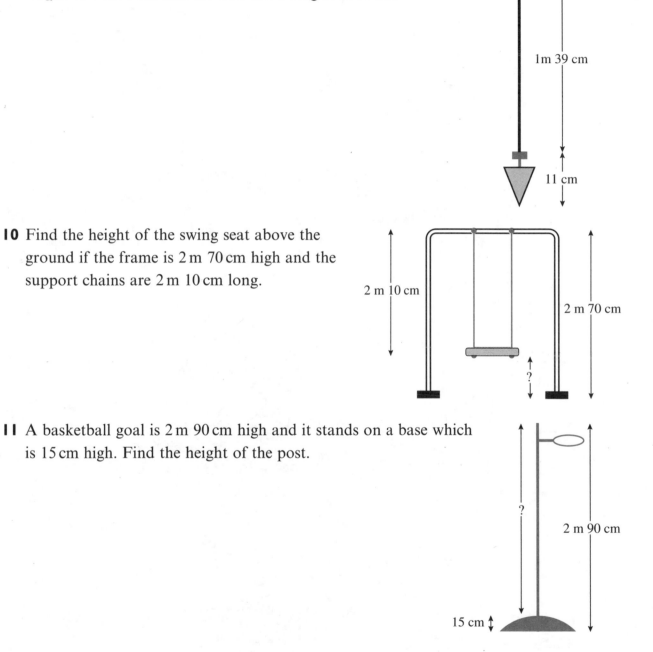

10 Find the height of the swing seat above the ground if the frame is 2 m 70 cm high and the support chains are 2 m 10 cm long.

11 A basketball goal is 2 m 90 cm high and it stands on a base which is 15 cm high. Find the height of the post.

12 A fence post is 2 m 20 cm high and is beaten into the ground so that 1 m 40 cm projects above the ground. What length is hammered into the ground ?

12 Weight

12 A *Idea of mass and weight: language, comparison and order*

The main units of mass are the kilogram and the gram.

One kilogram (kg) is the mass of a standard sized bag of sugar.

One gram (g) is the mass of four matchsticks.

There are 1000 grams in 1 kilogram: $1\,kg = 1000\,g$.

1 Does a packet of crisps have a mass of about 25 grams ?

2 Is the mass of this book more or less than one kilogram ?

3 Estimate in grams the mass of your shoes.

4 Estimate in kilograms the mass of yourself.

5 Which of the two objects is the heavier ?

a    b

6 Put the objects below in order of mass, starting with the lightest.

A    B

C    D

12 B *Using scales to weigh objects in grams and kilograms*

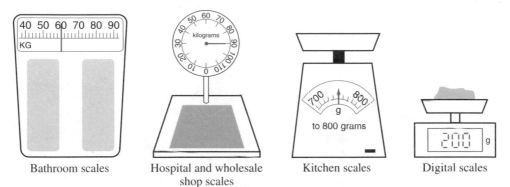

Bathroom scales   Hospital and wholesale   Kitchen scales   Digital scales
shop scales

1 Do the bathroom scales above show a mass or weight of 60 kg ?

2 What weight is shown on:
   a the hospital scales   **b** the kitchen scales   **c** the digital scales ?

3 What weight is shown on each of these scales:

a
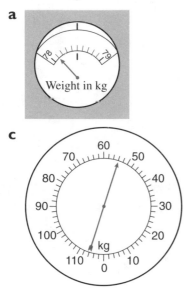

b

c
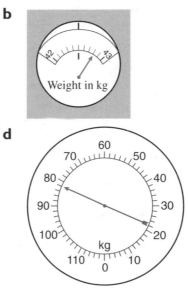

d

4 Do you agree that the weight shown
on this scale is 220 grams ?

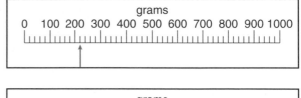

5 What three weights are shown on
this scale ?

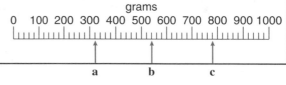

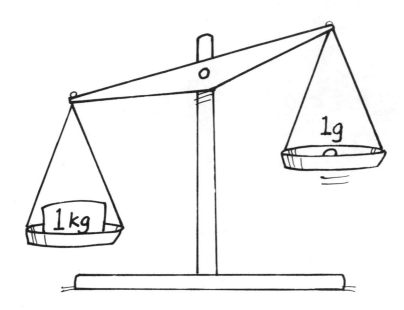

1 a Do you agree that there are 1000 grams in 1 kilogram ?

  b Copy and complete the statement: 1 kilogram = ____ grams.

2 How many grams are there in:

    a 2 kg   **b** 5 kg   **c** 1 kg and 200 g

    d 1 kg and 590 g   **e** 2 kg and 300 g   **f** 3 kg and 430 g ?

3 How many kilograms are there in:

    a 4000 g   **b** 9000 g ?

4 How many kilograms and grams are there in:

    a 1400 g   **b** 1600 g   **c** 3640 g   **d** 3075 g   **e** 4050 g   **f** 6007 g ?

Example

1.235 kg means 1 kg and 235 g

2.070 kg means 2 kg and 70 g

---

5 Write the number of kg and g in:

   a 1.435 kg   **b** 2.159 kg   **c** 3.536 kg

   d 3.530 kg   **e** 4.600 kg   **f** 1.030 kg

6 Write as _·___ kg

   a 1535 g   **b** 5246 g   **c** 2750 g   **d** 3250 g   **e** 5400 g   **f** 5004 g

7 How many grams are there in:

   a 1.652 kg   **b** 3.217 kg   **c** 6.52 kg   **d** 9.18 kg   **e** 4.05 kg   **f** 6.2 kg ?

8 Put the following in order starting with the largest.

   3202 g, 3.200 kg, 3022 g, 3.020 kg, 3002 g, 3.220 kg, 3222 g

12 D *Addition and subtraction of weights*

I Find:
  a 26 g + 53 g   **b** 87 g + 45 g   **c** 250 g + 150 g   **d** 650 g + 175 g

2 Add together:
  a 12 kg and 69 kg   **b** 36 kg and 49 kg   **c** 78 kg and 62 kg   **d** 150 kg and 95 kg

3 Find the sum of:
  a 1200 g and 1500 g   **b** 5380 g and 2970 g
  c 2895 g and 3355 g   **d** 4935 g and 3815 g

4 A packet of butter weighs 250 g. A jar of honey weighs 450 g.
What do the two weigh together ?

5 Ahmed cuts a tree branch in two pieces. One weighs 76 kg, the
other weighs 57 kg. What was the original weight of the wood ?

6 Dan's car weighs 1800 kg. His caravan weighs 1200 kg. What is
the total weight of the two when he is towing his caravan ?

7 Find:

    a 35 g – 17 g   **b** 96 g – 38 g   **c** 350 g – 200 g   **d** 705 g – 150 g

8 Subtract 25 kg from:

    a 39 kg   **b** 147 kg

    Subtract 45 kg from:

    c 463 kg   **d** 330 kg

9 Find the difference between:

    a 2500 g and 1300 g   **b** 7100 g and 3800 g

    c 3400 g and 900 g   **d** 1500 g and 75 g

10 Mark weighs 63 kg. Ian weighs 48 kg.

    How much lighter is Ian ?

11 A packet of butter weighs 500 g.

    A small jar of coffee weighs 275 g.

    How much heavier is the butter ?

12 A rubbish skip can carry 4000 kg.

    A builder part fills it with 2400 kg of rubble.

    What extra weight can the skip still carry ?

13 A lift in a hotel can carry 500 kg. Three people of weights 55 kg,
60 kg and 75 kg get in. How much luggage can the lift carry
without being overloaded ?

I   A torch weighs 95 g. The battery required for it weighs 25 g. What
is the weight of the torch when it is operating ?

2   A jam jar weighs 105 g when empty and holds 495 g of jam.
What is the weight of the full jar ?

3   Marcus weighs 75 kg. He has a bicycle of weight 15 kg.
What is the total weight when he rides his bicycle ?

4   My car weighs 2250 kg and it is towing a trailer of weight 550 kg.
What is the total weight of the car and trailer ?

5   Some mortar is mixed by adding 12 kg of cement to 38 kg of sand
and 2 kg of water. What is the weight of the mortar ?

6 My dog weighs 30 kg and my cat weighs 11 kg.
How much heavier is my dog ?

7 A full carton of milk weighs 590 g and the milk itself weighs 568 g. What is the weight of the empty carton ?

8 A copper pan weighs 510 g whereas a similar aluminium one weighs only 160 g. How much lighter is the aluminium pan ?

9 A van can carry a maximum load of 500 kg. A builder has placed 420 kg of sand in it.
Find the weight of the heaviest driver who can drive the van.

10 A small boat can carry a maximum load of only 250 kg. Three people of weights 80, 60 and 65 kg are sitting in it.
What is the weight of the heaviest person that can still board the boat ?

11 Mumbi's doll's push-chair weighs 7 kg 500 g. Her doll weighs 750 g. What weight does she push if the doll is in its push-chair ?

12 A mop head weighs 600 g and the handle weighs 500 g. What is the weight of the mop in kilograms and grams ?

13 A large gate is locked by a heavy padlock and chain. If the padlock weighs 325 g and the chain weighs 775 g, find the total weight (in kg and g) of the lock and chain.

14 A table lamp weighs 1 kg 110 g. Its bulb weighs 25 g and its shade weighs 65 g. What is the total weight of the complete lamp ?

15 A can full of petrol weighs 4 kg 60 g. The empty can weighs 110 g. What is the weight of the petrol ?

16 A hose pipe reel weighs 5 kg 400 g when the hose is wound on it and 1 kg 250 g when it is empty. Find the weight of the hose pipe.

17 A bicycle wheel, without the tyre pumped up, weighs 1 kg 995 g. When the tyre is pumped up the weight increases to 2 kg 3 g. What weight of air has been pumped into the tyre ?

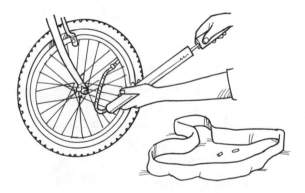

18 A room dryer has a plastic container of weight 105 g. After being used for a week the container is full of water and weighs 5 kg 75 g. Find the weight of water that the dryer collected.

13 Reading scales

13 A Scales marked in units and half-units

1 Write down the length shown by each arrow on the scale.
The scale is marked in centimetres.

```
0   1   2   3   4   5   6   7   8   9   10
          ↑       ↑   ↑           ↑
          a       d   b           c
```

2 Copy the scale and use an arrow to indicate each length.

```
0   1   2   3   4   5   6   7   8   9   10
```

The scale is marked in centimetres.

a 3 cm   **b** 6 cm   **c** 9 cm   **d** 7 cm

3 Write down the length shown by each arrow on the scale.
The scale is marked in centimetres and half centimetres.

```
0   1   2   3   4   5   6   7   8   9   10
          ↑           ↑   ↑       ↑
          a           b   d       c
```

4 Copy the scale and use an arrow to indicate each length.

```
0   1   2   3   4   5   6   7   8   9   10
```

The scale is marked in centimetres and half centimetres.

a 4.5 cm   **b** 7.5 cm   **c** 9.5 cm   **d** 1.5 cm

5 Write down the weight shown by each arrow on the scale opposite. The scale is marked in kilograms and half kilograms.

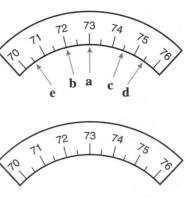

6 Copy the scale opposite and use an arrow to indicate each weight. The scale is marked in kilograms and half kilograms.

a 71 kg   **b** 74 kg   **c** 70 kg   **d** 73.5 kg

7 Copy the scale and use an arrow to indicate each
weight. The scale is marked in intervals of five
kilograms.

Each of the following members of the Jones family
stands on the weighing machine.

a Mr. Jones, 80 kg   **b** Bob Jones, 65 kg
c Monica Jones, 25 kg   **d** Smudge the cat, 5 kg

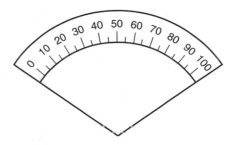

8 Copy the scale and use an arrow to indicate each
weight. The scale is marked in intervals of half
kilograms.

Each of the following is placed on a set of kitchen
scales.

a A large bag of cooking apples, 4 kg
b A large drum of salt, 2.5 kg
c A bag of potatoes, 7.5 kg
d A pack of margarine, 0.5 kg

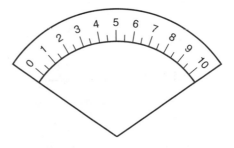

9 A weighing machine at a post office has the scale
illustrated. It is marked in intervals of 5 kg.
Copy the scale and use an arrow to indicate the
weight of each of the following parcels.

a 40 kg   **b** 15 kg   **c** 25 kg   **d** 5 kg

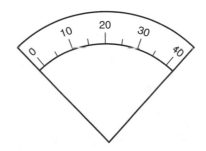

10 A weighing machine at a nursery has a scale as shown
on the right. It is marked in half gram intervals.
Copy the scale and use an arrow to indicate the
weight of each of the seed packets shown below.

a 4 g   **b** 9 g   **c** 3.8 g   **d** 8.5 g

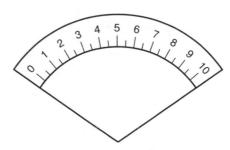

13 B *Scales marked in 2, 5 or 10 units*

I Write down the length shown by each arrow on the scale. The scale is marked in 2 cm intervals with 1 cm intervals indicated.

2 Copy the scale and use an arrow to indicate each length. The scale is marked in 2 cm intervals with 1 cm intervals indicated.

a 6 cm   **b** 11 cm   **c** 19 cm   **d** 9 cm

3 Write down the length shown by each arrow on the scale. The scale is marked in 5 cm intervals with 1 cm intervals indicated.

4 Copy the scale and use an arrow to indicate each length. The scale is marked in 5 cm intervals with 1 cm intervals indicated.

a 7 cm   **b** 21 cm   **c** 48 cm   **d** 13 cm

5 Write down the length shown by each arrow on the scale. The scale is marked in 10 mm intervals with 1 mm intervals indicated.

6 Copy the scale and use an arrow to indicate each length. The scale is marked in 10 mm intervals with 1 mm intervals indicated.

a 25 mm   **b** 75 mm   **c** 38 mm   **d** 87 mm   **e** 9 mm   **f** 21 mm

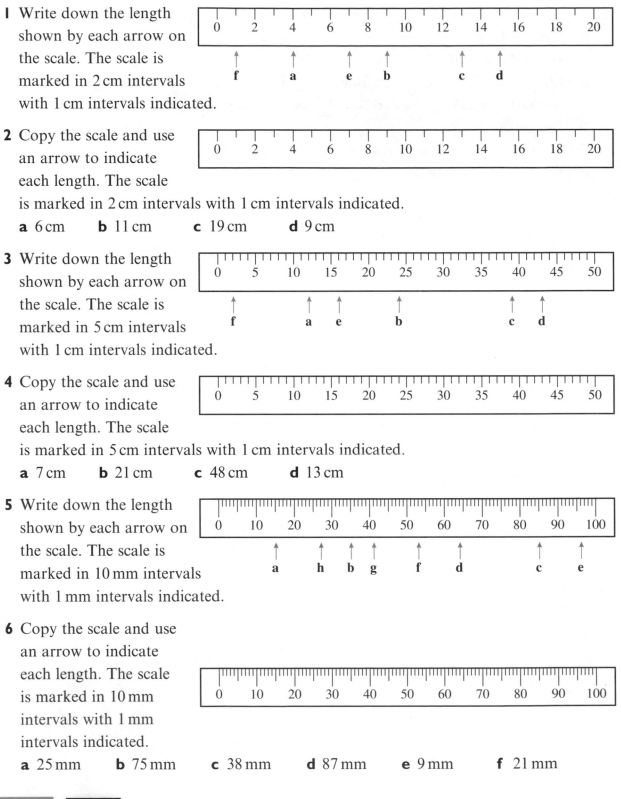

COPY ⊘

7 Copy the dial illustrated and mark with an arrow the position of the pointer when each of the following stand on the weighing machine. The dial is marked in 10 kg intervals with 2 kg intervals indicated.

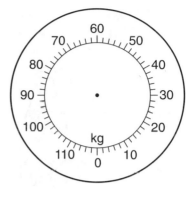

a Peter Brown, 50 kg
b Jane Brown, 44 kg
c Mr. Brown, 82 kg
d Mrs. Brown, 68 kg
e Marcus Brown, 20 kg
f Patch the dog, 14 kg

8 Copy the dial illustrated and mark with an arrow the position of the pointer when each of the following are placed on the kitchen scales. The dial is marked in 0.5 kg intervals with 0.1 kg intervals indicated.

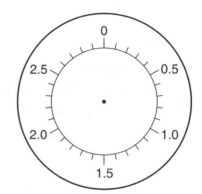

a A bag of apples, 2.5 kg
b A large pack of butter, 1.6 kg
c A bottle of lemonade, 0.8 kg
d A carton of yoghurt, 0.3 kg

9 A weighing machine at a post office has the scale illustrated. It is marked in 50 g intervals with 10 g intervals indicated. Copy the scale and mark with an arrow the position of the pointer when letters of each of the following weights are placed on it.

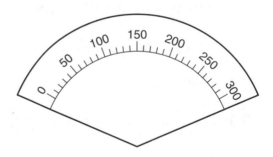

a 150 g   **b** 180 g   **c** 240 g   **d** 50 g

14 Capacity

14 A Idea of capacity: language, comparison and order

The main units of capacity are the litre, centilitre and millilitre.

One litre (ℓ) is the capacity of a standard size bottle of squash.

One centilitre (cℓ) is the capacity of two medicine spoons.

There are one hundred centilitres in one litre: $1\,\ell = 100\,\text{c}\ell$.

One millilitre (mℓ) of water has a mass of one gram.

There are one thousand millilitres in a litre: $1\,\ell = 1000\,\text{m}\ell$.

There are ten millilitres in a centilitre: $1\,\ell = 10\,\text{m}\ell$.

1 Does a large carton of milk have a capacity of about 1 litre ?

2 Is the capacity of your teapot more or less than one litre ?

3 Estimate in millilitres how much a standard matchbox will hold.

4 Estimate in centilitres how much your tea cup will hold.

5 Estimate in litres how much water your bath will hold.

6

a Which object has a greatest capacity ?
b Which object has the least capacity ?
c Put the objects in order of capacity with the smallest first.

14 B   *Using containers to measure capacities*

I Does the tumbler above show a capacity of 250 mℓ ?

2 What is the capacity shown on:
   a the measuring jug   **b** the chemist's measuring flask ?

3 What "amount" is shown on each of these measuring jugs ?
   a   **b**

4 What amount is shown on each of these measuring flasks ?
   a   **b**

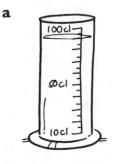

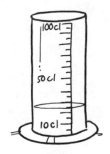

5 State in millilitres the amount of liquid in each container.
   a   **b**

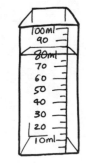

14 c *Converting between millilitres, centilitres and litres*

1 a Do you agree that there are 10 millilitres in one centilitre ?
  b Copy and complete the statement: $1\,c\ell = \underline{}\,m\ell$.

2 How many millilitres are there in:
  a $2\,c\ell$ **b** $8\,c\ell$?

3 How many centilitres are there in:
  a $40\,m\ell$ **b** $70\,m\ell$?

4 a Do you agree that there are 100 centilitres in one litre ?
  b Copy and complete the statement: $1\,\ell = \underline{}\,c\ell$.

5 How many centilitres are there in:
  a $3\,\ell$ **b** $5\,\ell$ **c** $1\,\ell$ and $27\,c\ell$ **d** $5\,\ell$ and $50\,c\ell$?

6 How many litres are there in:
  a $600\,c\ell$ **b** $2000\,c\ell$?

7 How many litres and centilitres are there in:
  a $140\,c\ell$ **b** $164\,c\ell$ **c** $238\,c\ell$ **d** $572\,c\ell$?

1.23 ℓ means 1 ℓ and 23 cℓ
2.07 ℓ means 2 ℓ and 7 cℓ

8 Write the number of l and cl in:
   a 1.43 ℓ **b** 2.61 ℓ **c** 6.15 ℓ **d** 1.03 ℓ

9 Write as _._ _ ℓ:
   a 153 cℓ **b** 256 cℓ **c** 734 cℓ **d** 240 cℓ **e** 802 cℓ **f** 101 cℓ

10 How many centilitres are there in:
   a 1.93 ℓ **b** 2.71 ℓ **c** 4.30 ℓ **d** 9.70 ℓ **e** 1.03 ℓ **f** 5.09 ℓ ?

1 Find:
   a 26 mℓ + 53 mℓ   **b** 39 mℓ + 25 mℓ   **c** 360 mℓ + 240 mℓ   **d** 455 mℓ + 345 mℓ

2 Add together:
   a 12 cℓ and 69 cℓ   **b** 35 cℓ and 56 cℓ   **c** 25 cℓ and 225 cℓ   **d** 150 cℓ and 450 cℓ

3 Find the sum of:
   a 120 ℓ and 150 ℓl   **b** 340 ℓ and 170 ℓ   **c** 125 ℓ and 375 ℓ   **d** 125 ℓ and 75 ℓ

4 A bottle of sauce has a capacity of 250 mℓ.
   A larger bottle of the same sauce has a capacity of 330 mℓ.
   What capacity do the two have together ?

5 Dan's aeroplane has two fuel tanks.
   The main tank can hold 2500 ℓ and the reserve
   tank can hold 1200 ℓ.
   What is the total capacity of the two fuel tanks ?

6 Find:

    a 36 mℓ − 17 mℓ   **b** 95 mℓ − 38 mℓ   **c** 450 mℓ − 290 mℓ   **d** 600 mℓ − 125 mℓ

7 Subtract 23 cℓ from:

    a 39 cℓ   **b** 91 cℓ   **c** 147 cℓ   **d** 250 cℓ

8 Find the difference between:

    a 2300 l and 1500 l   **b** 7200 l and 2500 l

    c 4000 ℓ and 250 ℓ   **d** 3000 ℓ and 750 ℓ

9 The fuel tank on a Wolf car has a capacity of 65 ℓ.

The fuel tank on a Fox car has a capacity of 47 ℓ.

How much less fuel does the Fox car hold ?

10 Three people have drinks from a 1.5 ℓ (1500 mℓ) bottle of lemonade.

The amounts of these drinks are: 250 mℓ, 475 mℓ and 600 mℓ.

How much lemonade will be left in the bottle ?

1 Anish is doing a chemistry experiment. He has 37 mℓ of solution in a flask and he adds a further 28 mℓ from a burette. How many millilitres does he have in the flask now ?

2 One night a rain-gauge held 380 mℓ of water. The next morning it held 460 ml. How many millilitres of rain were added overnight ?

3 There are 18 litres of petrol in my car's tank. I fill it up at a garage where I have to put in an extra 32 litres. How many litres does the tank hold altogether ?

4 A barman has two barrels of "Best Brew Bitter", one contains 150 litres and the other 40 litres. How many litres does he have to sell ?

5 A large tea urn contained 28 litres of tea when a cafe opened in the morning. By early afternoon there were only 19 litres left. How many litres were sold ?

6 A railway locomotive has 800 litres of diesel in its tank at the start of a journey. At the end of the journey there were 550 litres left. How many litres were used during the journey ?

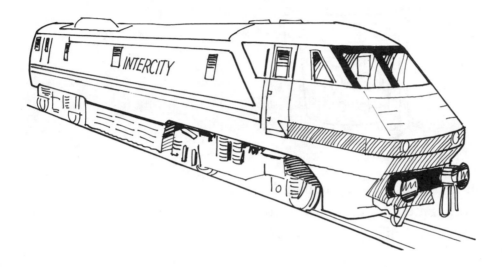

7 A small can of "Superloob" contains 115 mℓ of oil, whereas a small can of "Slipwell" only contains 96 mℓ. How many more millilitres of oil does the first can hold ?

8 A measuring beaker with 95 mℓ of water was placed in a freezer. When the water was completely frozen the level was up to 110 mℓ. By how many millilitres did the water expand on freezing ?

9 A party can of Coke contained 31 500 mℓ when full but after a party there were 11 250 mℓ left.
How much Coke had been drunk at the party ?

10 An ice cream seller has a can containing 41 500 mℓ of ice cream. After a sunny afternoon there are only 750 mℓ left.
How much did she sell ?

11 Mrs. Khan has a plastic bottle containing 11 500 mℓ of cooking oil. After pouring some into a chip pan there are 950 mℓ left in the bottle. How many millilitres did she use ?

12 Mrs. Green has a saucepan with markings on it. In order to boil some eggs she filled it to the 11 250 mℓ mark. After she had hard-boiled the eggs the water level had fallen to the 750 mℓ mark.
How much water had boiled away ?

13 Mrs. Ahmed has made some jam. She finds that it exactly fills three jars, one of capacity 1 ℓ 500 mℓ, one of capacity 1 ℓ 250 mℓ and one of capacity 1 ℓ 750 mℓ. How much jam has she made?

14 Sanjay is making some dilute sulphuric acid in the chemistry laboratory. He carefully adds 150 mℓ of concentrated acid to 1 ℓ 750 mℓ of water. How much dilute acid does he make up?

15 A paraffin heater has a tank marked "Capacity 3 litres". When the gauge is showing 1 ℓ 250 mℓ, John finds that he needs 1 ℓ 750 mℓ to fill the tank up. Are the markings correct?

16 Jean, Meg and Peter fill glasses with respective capacities of 150 mℓ, 180 mℓ and 220 mℓ with lemonade and find that they exactly empty a full bottle. What was the capacity of the bottle?

15 Angles

15 A Understanding clockwise and anticlockwise ($\frac{1}{4}$, $\frac{1}{2}$ and $\frac{3}{4}$ turns)

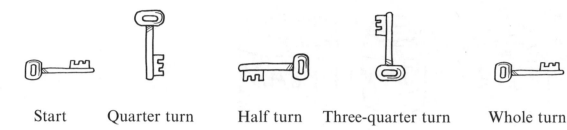

Start   Quarter turn   Half turn   Three-quarter turn   Whole turn

1 The first arrow below has made a quarter turn clockwise.
Write down how far each of the other arrows has turned.

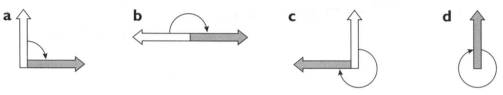

a   **b**   **c**   **d**

2 Say whether the arrow has turned clockwise or anticlockwise.

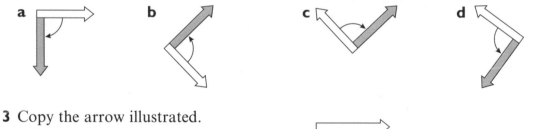

a   **b**   **c**   **d**

3 Copy the arrow illustrated.
Draw its new position after:
a a quarter turn clockwise
b a half turn
c a three-quarter turn anticlockwise.

4 Look at the compass points on the right.
What turn **i** clockwise and **ii** anticlockwise
do I need to make when I move from:
a N to E   **b** N to W   **c** E to W
d E to S   **e** S to E   **f** S to W ?

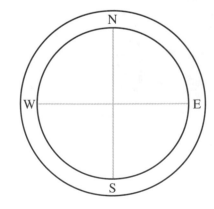

15 B *Recognising right angles and angles of more or less than 90°*

A complete turn is divided into 360 parts called degrees.

1 complete turn = 360°   1 half turn = 180°

1 quarter turn = 90°   3 quarters of a turn = 270°

A quarter turn, or a turn of 90°, is called a right angle.

I Say which of the following angles is a **right angle**.

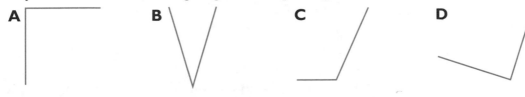

2 Look again at the angles in Question **I**. Say which angles are:

  a less than 90°   **b** more than 90°

3 What is the smaller angle between the hands of a clock at 9 a.m. ?
  What is the larger angle at this time ?

4 Through what angle does the hour hand of a clock move
  between:

  a 12 o'clock and 3 o'clock

  b 12 o'clock and 6 o'clock

  c 12 o'clock and 9 o'clock

  d in twelve hours ?

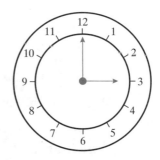

5 Through what angle does the hour hand of a clock move:

  a between 3 o'clock and   **i** 6 o'clock   **ii** 9 o'clock   **iii** 12 o'clock

  b in   **i** 6 hours   **ii** 3 hours   **iii** 9 hours ?

6 Through what angle in a clockwise direction does the
  wind turn if it changes direction from:

  a N to E   **b** N to S

  c E to W   **d** S to E

  e W to N   **f** W to S ?

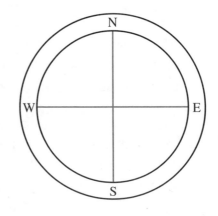

15 C *Recognising acute, obtuse and reflex angles*

An angle which is less than 90° is called an acute angle.

An obtuse angle is more than 90° but less than 180°.

A reflex angle is more than 180° but less than a complete turn.

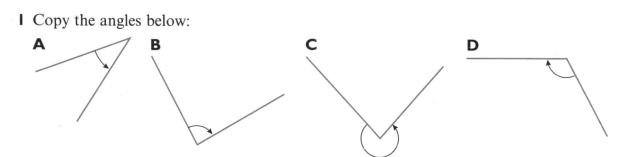

1 Copy the angles below:

A   **B**   **C**   **D**

    a Which of the angles are less than 90° ?
       Label these acute angles.
    b Which of the angles are more than 90° but less than 180° ?
       Label these obtuse angles.
    c Which of the angles are more than 180° ?
       Label these reflex angles.

2 Draw:
    a an acute angle   **b** another larger acute angle
    c an obtuse angle   **d** another smaller obtuse angle
    e a reflex angle   **f** another larger reflex angle.

3 Say whether each angle is:
    i an acute angle   **ii** a right angle   **iii** an obtuse angle
    a 63°   **b** 90°   **c** 123°   **d** 45°   **e** 160°   **f** 5°

15 D   *Estimating angles to the nearest 10°*

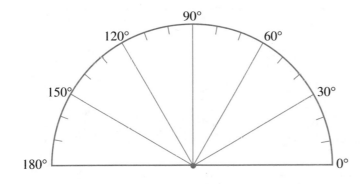

1 Estimate the size of each angle to the nearest 10°.

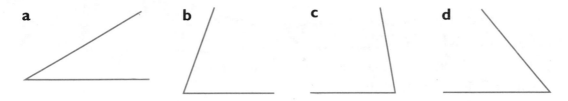

a   b   c   d

2 Estimate the size of each angle to the nearest 10°.

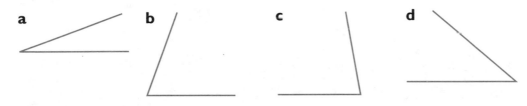

a   b   c   d

3 Estimate the size of each angle to the nearest 10°.

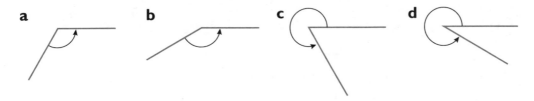

a   b   c   d

15 E *Using a protractor to measure angles to the nearest 3°*

Example

Measure the size of $P\widehat{Q}R$.

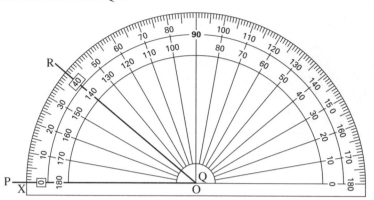

i Place the protractor on the angle so that O (the centre) is on Q, as shown above, and OX (the base line) lies on PQ.

ii Where the line QR cuts the scale, read off the angle on the outer scale, starting from 0° at P.

iii $P\widehat{Q}R = 40°$.

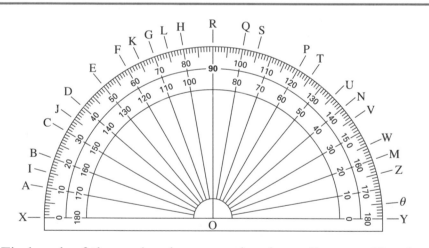

1 Find each of the angles shown on the above diagram. Use the information to complete the table below.

a $X\widehat{O}A = 10°$ $X\widehat{O}B = 20°$ $X\widehat{O}C =$ $X\widehat{O}D =$

b $X\widehat{O}E =$ $X\widehat{O}F = 60°$ $X\widehat{O}G =$ $X\widehat{O}H =$

c $X\widehat{O}I = 15°$ $X\widehat{O}J =$ $X\widehat{O}K =$ $X\widehat{O}L =$

d $Y\widehat{O}M = 20°$ $Y\widehat{O}N =$ $Y\widehat{O}P =$ $Y\widehat{O}Q =$

e $Y\widehat{O}R =$ $Y\widehat{O}S = 75°$ $Y\widehat{O}T =$ $Y\widehat{O}U =$

f $Y\widehat{O}V =$ $Y\widehat{O}W =$ $Y\widehat{O}Z =$ $Y\widehat{O}\theta =$

Use a protractor to measure each of the following angles.

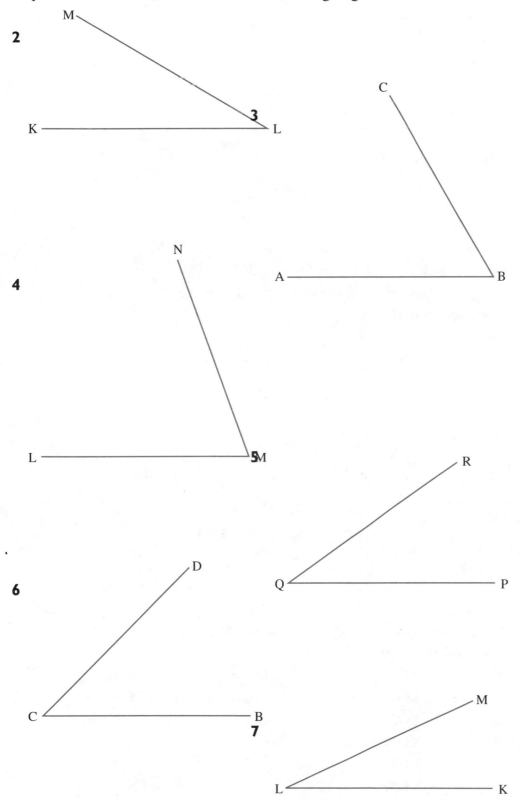

2

3

4

6

7

Measure the size of angle $\widehat{LMN}$.

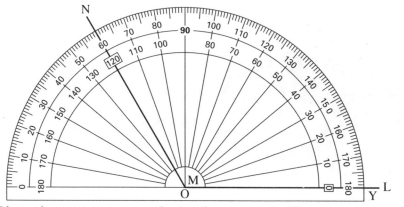

i   Place the protractor on the angle so that O (the centre) is on M, as shown above, and OY (the base line) lies on ML.

ii   Where the line MN cuts the scale, read off the angle on the inner scale, starting from 0° at L.

iii $\widehat{LMN} = 120°$.

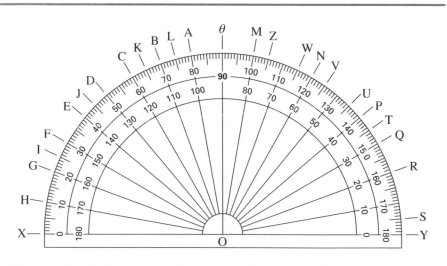

8 Find each of the angles shown on the above diagram.
Use the information to complete the table below.

a $\widehat{YOA} = 100°$ $\widehat{YOB} =$ $\widehat{YOC} =$ $\widehat{YOD} =$

b $\widehat{YOE} =$ $\widehat{YOF} =$ $\widehat{YOG} =$ $\widehat{YOH} =$

c $\widehat{YOI} = 155°$ $\widehat{YOJ} =$ $\widehat{YOK} =$ $\widehat{YOL} =$

d $\widehat{XOM} = 100°$ $\widehat{XON} =$ $\widehat{XOP} =$ $\widehat{XOQ} =$

e $\widehat{XOR} =$ $\widehat{XOS} =$ $\widehat{XOT} =$ $\widehat{XOU} =$

f $\widehat{XOV} =$ $\widehat{XOW} =$ $\widehat{XOZ} =$ $\widehat{XO\theta} =$

Use a protractor to measure each of the following angles.

9

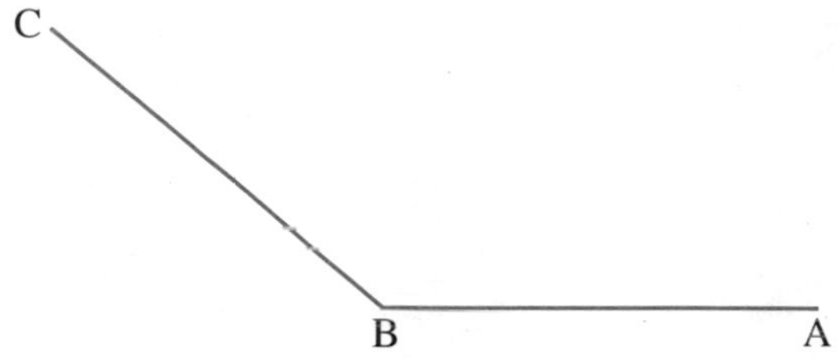

10

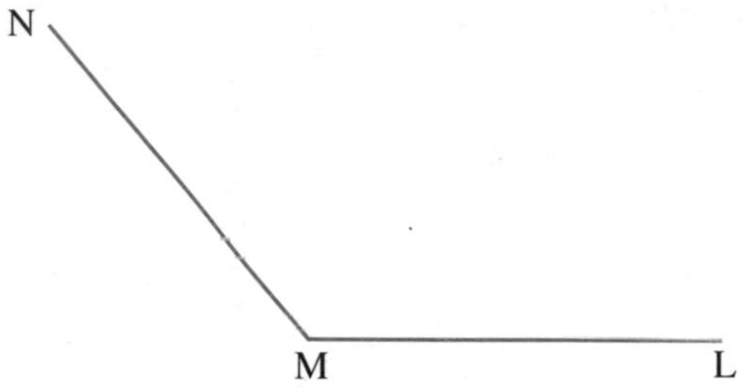

11

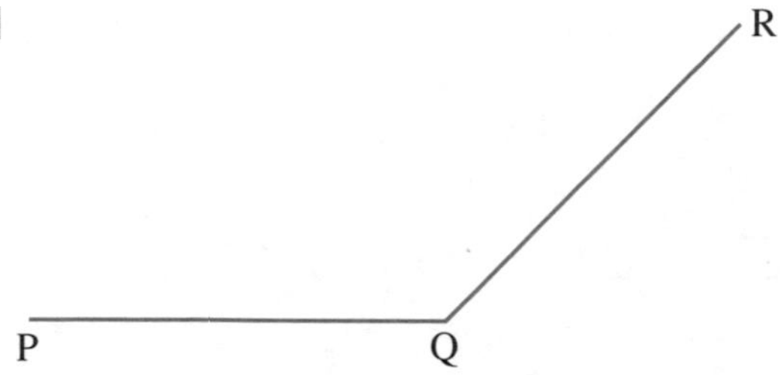

12

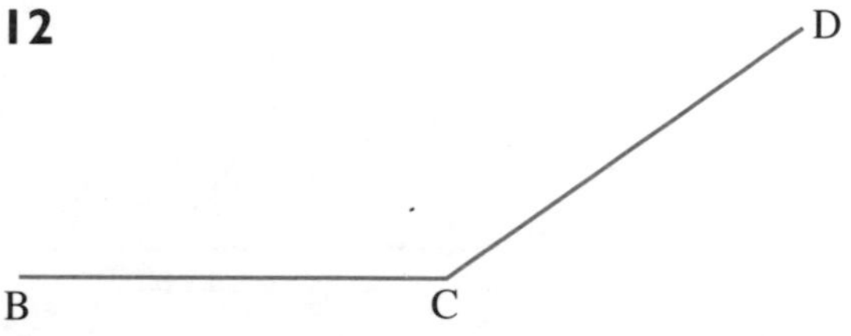

13

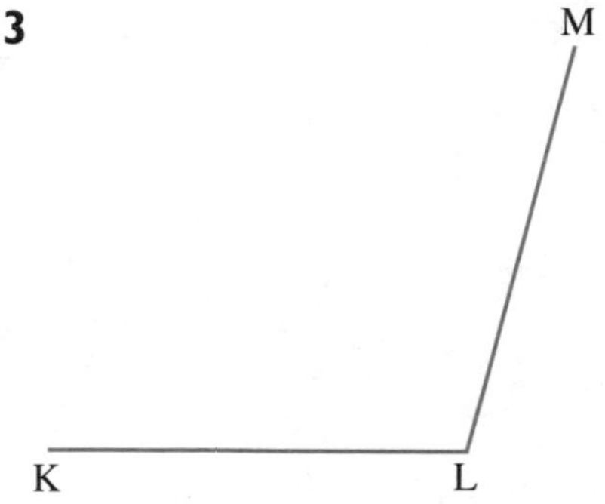

14

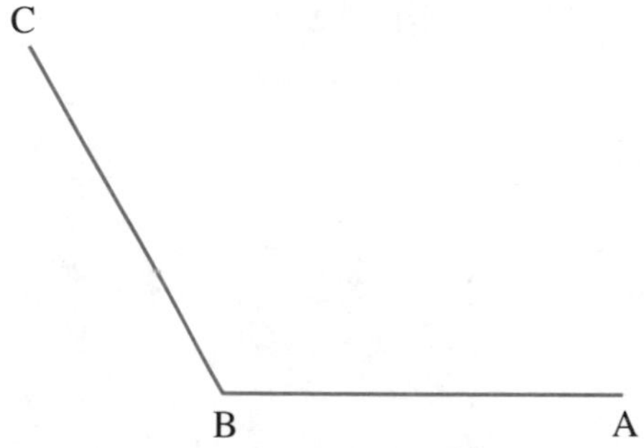

15 F *Using a protractor to draw angles to the nearest 3°*

Example

Using a protractor, draw **a** $\widehat{ABC} = 50°$ **b** $\widehat{XYZ} = 170°$

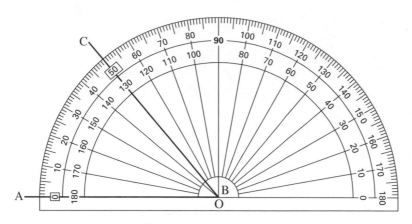

a i Draw the straight line AB. Make it 6 cm long.

   ii Place the protractor on the paper with its base line on the line AB and its centre point O on B as shown.

  iii Mark the point C at 50° on the scale starting from 0° at A.

  iv Join BC, and the angle 50° is now drawn complete.

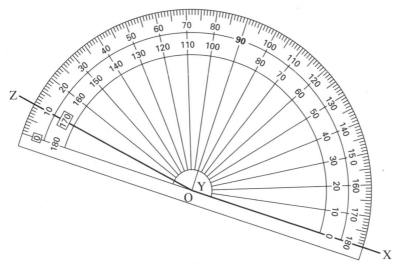

b i Draw the straight line XY. Make it 6 cm long.

   ii Place the protractor on the paper with its base line on the line XY and its centre point O on Y as shown.

  iii Mark the point Z at 170° on the scale starting from 0° at X.

  iv Join YZ and the angle of 170° is now drawn complete.

For each question, draw a line AB 6 cm long. Then draw the angle.

I Draw $A\widehat{B}C$ equal to 60°

2 Draw $A\widehat{B}C$ equal to 45°

3 Draw $A\widehat{B}C$ equal to 35°

4 Draw $B\widehat{A}C$ equal to 80°

5 Draw $B\widehat{A}C$ equal to 55°

6 Draw $A\widehat{B}C$ equal to 120°

7 Draw $A\widehat{B}C$ equal to 155°

8 Draw $A\widehat{B}C$ equal to 115°

9 Draw $B\widehat{A}C$ equal to 110°

10 Draw $B\widehat{A}C$ equal to 145°

Example _____

Draw a triangle with AB = 5 cm, $\widehat{A} = 50°$ and $\widehat{B} = 70°$.
Measure the third angle.

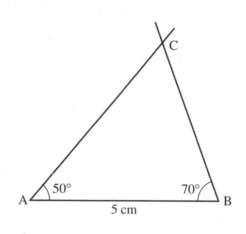

By measurement, $\widehat{C} = 60°$

_____

For each question, draw the triangle ABC from the details given.
Then measure the angle C with a protractor.

II AB = 5 cm, $\widehat{A} = 40°$, $\widehat{B} = 60°$

12 AB = 5 cm, $\widehat{A} = 50°$, $\widehat{B} = 40°$

13 AB = 5 cm, $\widehat{A} = 50°$, $\widehat{B} = 50°$

14 AB = 6 cm, $\widehat{A} = 30°$, $\widehat{B} = 40°$

15 AB = 6 cm, $\widehat{A} = 50°$, $\widehat{B} = 100°$

16 Plane shapes

Sorting and classifying two-dimensional shapes

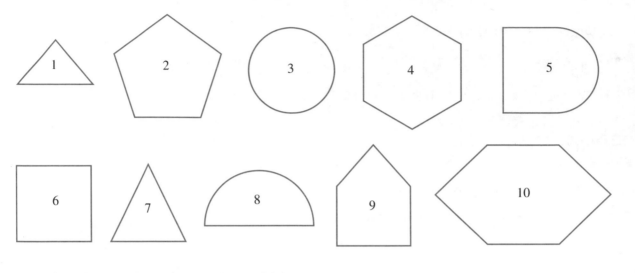

I Which shapes above have edges which are:
   a straight only   **b** curved only   **c** both straight and curved ?

2 Which shapes above have 3 straight edges ?
   These are called **triangles**.

3 Which shapes above have 5 straight edges ?
   These are called **pentagons**.

4 Which shapes above have 6 straight edges ?
   These are called **hexagons**.

5 Join each shape below with its name. One has been
   done for you. (Copy the details first.)

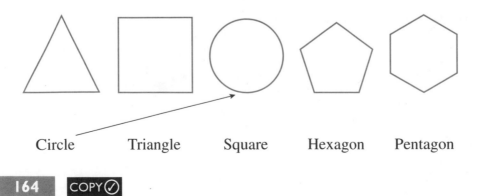

    Circle   Triangle   Square   Hexagon   Pentagon

COPY⊘

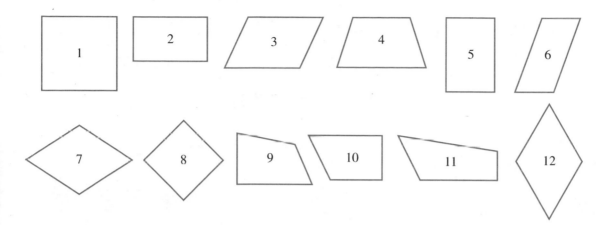

6 Which of the above shapes have 4 equal edges and 4 right angles ?
These are called **squares**.

7 Which of the above shapes have 4 right angles ?
These are called **rectangles**.

8 Which of the above shapes have 4 equal edges ?
These are called **rhombuses**.

9 Which of the above shapes have 2 pairs of parallel edges ?
Thcsc are called **parallelograms**.

10 Which of the above shapes have just one pair of parallel edges ?
These are called **trapeziums**.

11 Which of the shapes have no equal edges no pairs of parallel sides ?
These shapes are **irregular quadrilaterals**.

12 Join each shape with its name. One has been done for you.
(Copy the details first.)

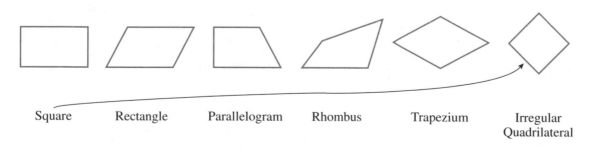

Square   Rectangle   Parallelogram   Rhombus   Trapezium   Irregular
Quadrilateral

Any shape made up entirely of straight lines is called a **polygon**.
When a shape has all its edges the same length and all its angles
the same size it is called a **regular polygon**.
Some well-known polygons are illustrated below.

A **triangle** is any shape with 3 edges.
(Tri- is the Latin name for three.)

A **quadrilateral** is any shape with 4 edges.
(Quad- is the Latin name for four.)

Regular triangle
(equilateral triangle)

Regular quadrilateral
(square)

Regular pentagon

A **pentagon** is any shape with 5 edges. (Pent- is the Latin name for five.)

Regular hexagon

A **hexagon** is any shape with 6 edges. (Hex- is the Latin name for six.)

Regular heptagon

A **heptagon** is any shape with 7 edges. (Hept- is the Latin name for seven.)

Regular octagon

An **octagon** is any shape with 8 edges. (Oct- is the Latin name for eight.)

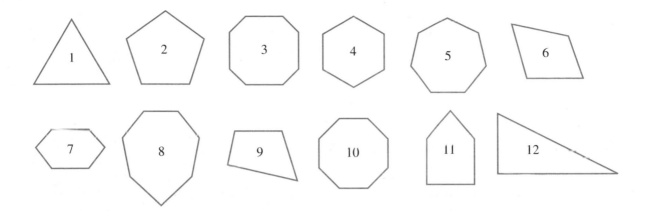

1 Which of the above shapes are triangles ?

2 Which of the above shapes are quadrilaterals ?

3 Which of the above shapes are pentagons ?

4 Which of the above shapes are hexagons ?

5 Which of the above shapes are heptagons ?

6 Which of the above shapes are octagons ?

7 Join each shape with its name. One has been done for you.
(Copy the details first.)

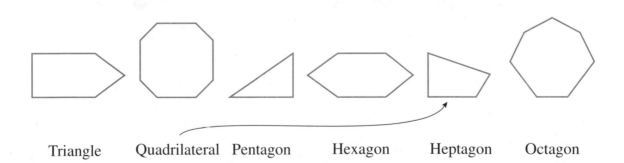

Triangle   Quadrilateral   Pentagon   Hexagon   Heptagon   Octagon

Triangles

Triangles can be classified in three ways by their angles.

i   A triangle may be **acute**-angled
(if all three angles are less than 90°).

iii   A triangle may be **obtuse**-angled
(if one angle is bigger than 90°).

iii   A triangle may be **right**-angled
(if one angle is equal to 90°).

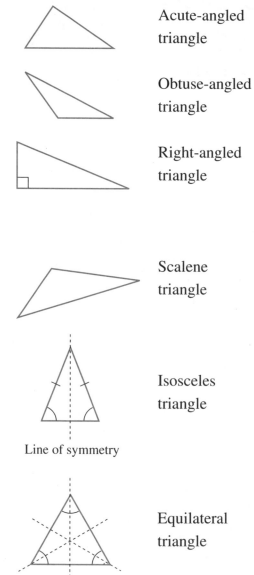

Acute-angled
triangle

Obtuse-angled
triangle

Right-angled
triangle

Triangles can also be classified according to their symmetry (or side lengths).

i   A triangle may be scalene, which means
that no angles or sides are equal and
therefore the triangle has no symmetry.

ii   A triangle may be isosceles, which means
that one pair of angles and one pair of sides
are equal and therefore the triangle has one
line of symmetry.

Scalene
triangle

Isosceles
triangle

Line of symmetry

iii   A triangle may be equilateral, which means
that all three angles and all three sides are
equal and therefore the triangle has three
lines of symmetry.

Equilateral
triangle

For each of the following, state whether the triangle is:
    a scalene, isosceles or equilateral   **b** acute-angled, obtuse-angled or right-angled.

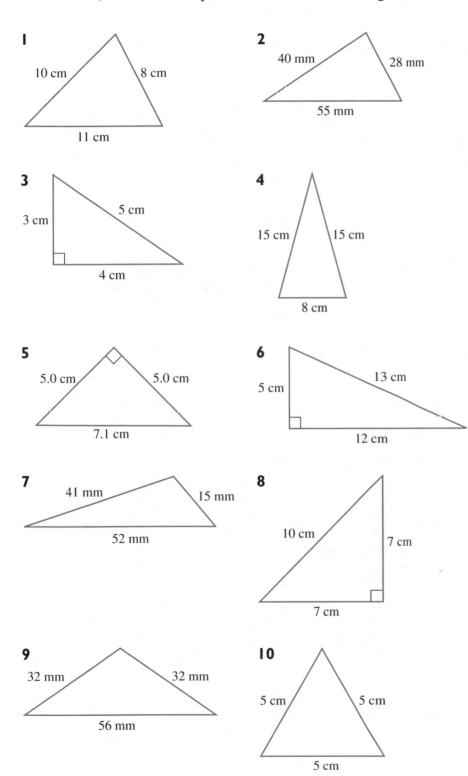

1
10 cm   8 cm
11 cm

2
40 mm   28 mm
55 mm

3
3 cm   5 cm
4 cm

4
15 cm   15 cm
8 cm

5
5.0 cm   5.0 cm
7.1 cm

6
5 cm   13 cm
12 cm

7
41 mm   15 mm
52 mm

8
10 cm   7 cm
7 cm

9
32 mm   32 mm
56 mm

10
5 cm   5 cm
5 cm

169

Quadrilaterals

Several kinds of quadrilaterals are illustrated below.

A **square** has 4 right angles and 4 edges the same length.

A **rectangle** has 4 right angles.

A **rhombus** has 4 edges the same length.

A **parallelogram** has two pairs of opposite edges which are parallel.

A **kite** has two pairs of adjacent edges (i.e. edges which are "next door" to each other) which are equal in length.

An **arrowhead** has the same properties as a kite, but one of the angles is a reflex angle (i.e. an angle bigger than 180°).

A **trapezium** has one pair of opposite edges which are parallel.

An **isosceles trapezium** is a trapezium whose non-parallel edges are equal in length.

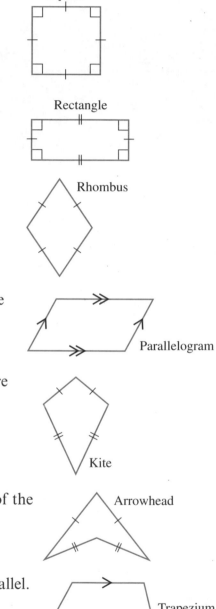

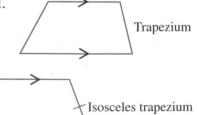

11 Copy the diagram below.
Join each shape to its name. The first one has been done for you.

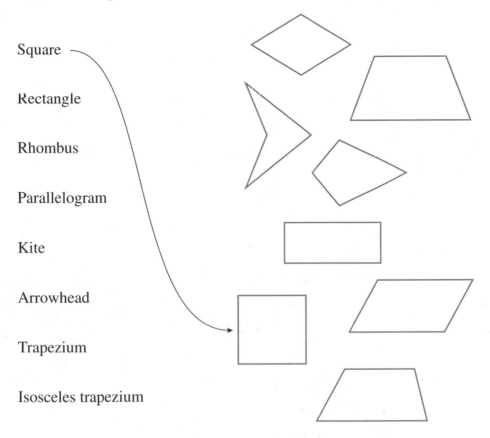

Square

Rectangle

Rhombus

Parallelogram

Kite

Arrowhead

Trapezium

Isosceles trapezium

12 If a quadrilateral is both a rectangle and a rhombus, it is a
_____.

13 If a quadrilateral is both a parallelogram and a kite, it is a
_____.

14 If a quadrilateral is both a parallelogram and an isosceles
trapezium it is a _____.

Under a **rotation** a shape
turns on to its new position.

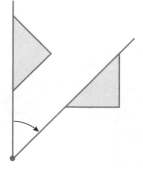

1 Through what angle has flag X been rotated in a clockwise
direction on to its new position Y ?

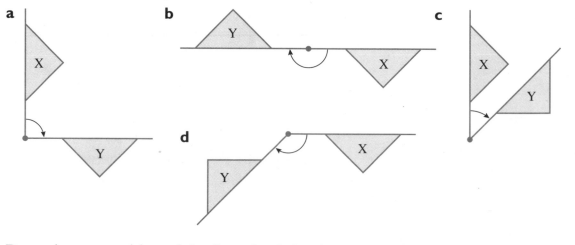

2 Draw the new position of the flag after it has been rotated
clockwise through
   a 90°   **b** 180°   **c** 45°   **d** 135°

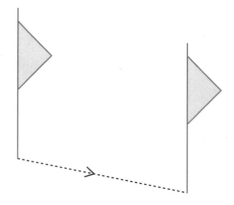

3 Repeat question **2** but instead rotate in an anticlockwise direction.

Under a **translation** a shape slides to
its new position without turning.

4 a Do you agree that the black duck has been translated 2 squares up to reach the position A ?

b Do you agree that the black duck has been translated 3 squares to the right to position B ?

c Describe the translation which moves the black duck on to:

   i position W   **ii** position X   **iii** position Y   **iv** position Z

5 Describe the translation on the right which moves the black duck on to the white duck in:

a position A   **b** position B
c position C   **d** position D

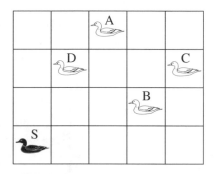

6 Copy the grid on the right. Show the position of the black duck after it has been translated:

a 3 squares to the right and 2 squares up
b 2 squares to the right and 1 square up
c 4 squares to the right and 1 square down
d 3 squares to the right only.

7 Look at the diagram on the right. Say whether flag A has been rotated or translated on to each of the other positions.

16 E *Simple tessellations*

A **tessellation** is a regularly repeating tiling pattern.
It can be made with one or more shapes which are
fitted together without leaving any gaps.
The one illustrated on the right is made with squares
and octagons.

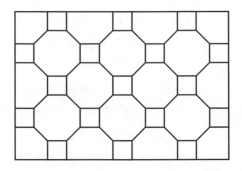

1 The tessellation of squares below has been started for you. Copy
   this and continue the pattern by adding another twelve squares.

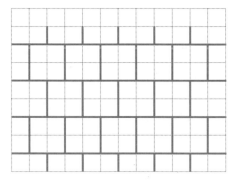

2 The tessellation of squares below has been started for you. Copy
   this and continue the pattern by adding another twelve squares.

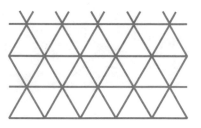

3 The tessellation of triangles below has been started for you. Copy
   this and continue the pattern by adding another twelve triangles.

4 The tessellation of hexagons has been started for you. Copy this and continue the pattern by adding another twelve hexagons.

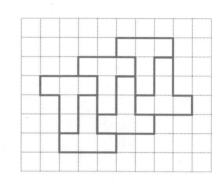

5 The tessellation of T's has been started for you. Copy this and continue the pattern by adding another twelve T's.

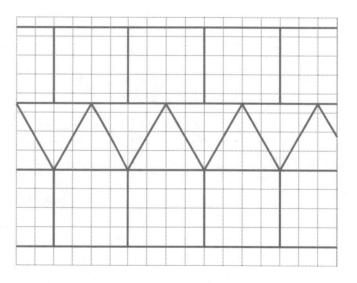

6 The tessellation of squares and triangles has been started for you. Copy this and continue the pattern by adding another six of each.

7 Copy the grid illustrated. One trapezium has been drawn for you. Fill the grid with trapeziums and make as many patterns as you can.

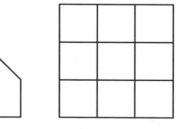

17 Symmetry

17 A *Continuing simple patterns made with shapes*

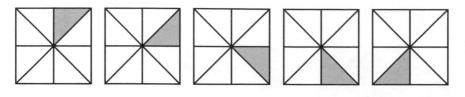

1 Look at the pattern above.
Do you agree that the next 3 shapes in the
pattern are the 3 shapes shown on the right ?

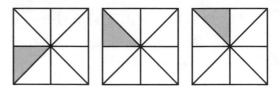

2 a Copy the next 3 shapes in the pattern below.

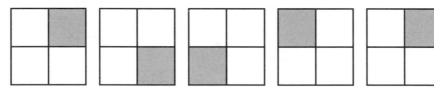

   b Draw the twelfth shape in this pattern.

3 a Copy the next 3 shapes in the pattern below.

   b Draw the twelfth shape in this pattern.

4 a Copy the next 3 shapes in the patterns below.

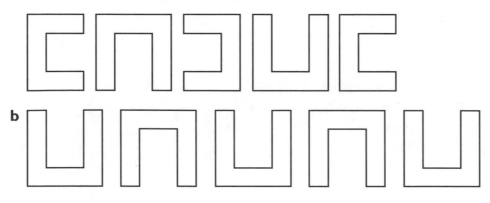

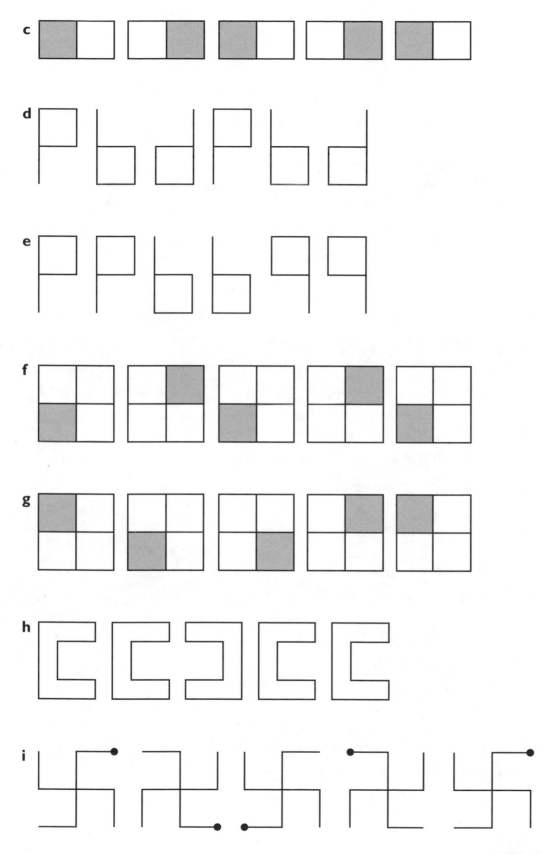

17 B   *Understanding reflection and line symmetry*

Reflections

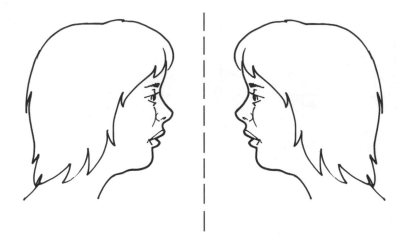

1 Look at the diagram above.

   a Do you agree that one head is the mirror image of the other ?

   b Do you agree that the mirror line is half way between the two heads ?

2 Copy each of the pictures below. Then draw in the mirror line so
that one shape is the mirror image of the other.

  a 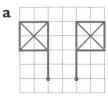   **b** 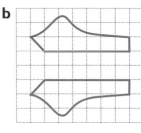   **c** 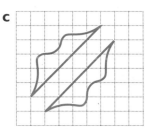   **d**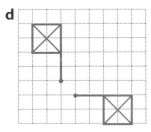

3 Copy the pictures below. Then draw the mirror image of the
shape using the dotted line as the mirror line.

  a 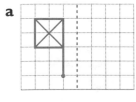   **b** 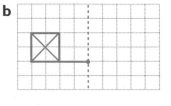   **c** 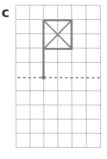   **d**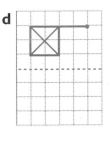

4 Copy each shape. Then draw the mirror image of the shape using the dotted line as the mirror line.

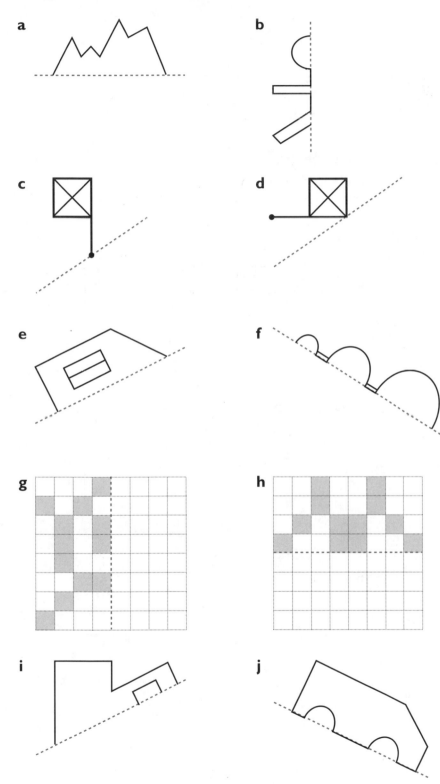

a

b

c

d

e

f

g

h

i

j

Line symmetry

kite

rectangle

5 Do you agree that:
   a the kite above has just one line of symmetry
   b the rectangle above has two lines of symmetry ?

6 Copy the shape and show its line of symmetry.

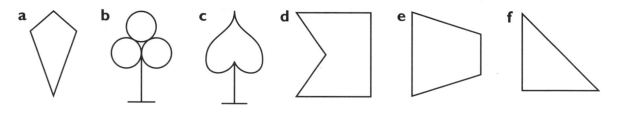

a   **b**   **c**   **d**   **e**   **f**

7 Copy the shape and show its two lines of symmetry.

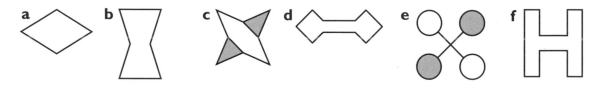

a   **b**   **c**   **d**   **e**   **f**

8 a Draw each of the capital letters of the alphabet.
   Mark on each letter any lines of symmetry.
   The letter A is shown on the right.
   b Which letters have no lines of symmetry ?

COPY ⊘

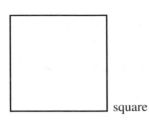 square

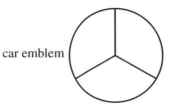 car emblem

9 Do you agree that:

   a the square above has four lines of symmetry

   b the car emblem above has three lines of symmetry ?

10 Look at each of the shapes below.

   a How many lines of symmetry does the shape have ?

   b Make a copy of the shape and mark all its lines of symmetry.

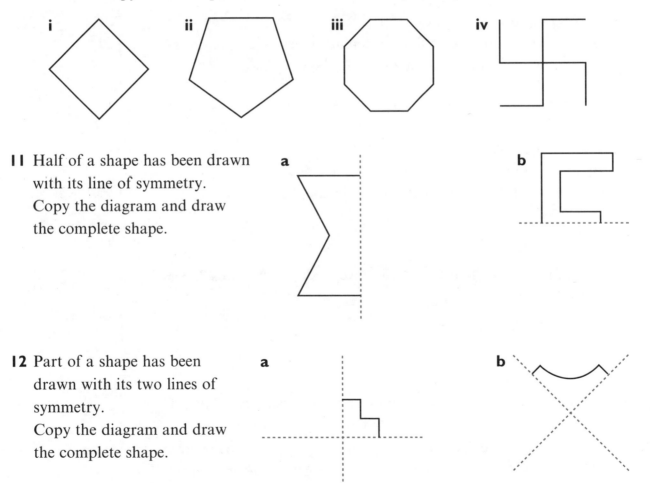

   i   ii   iii   iv

11 Half of a shape has been drawn with its line of symmetry.
Copy the diagram and draw the complete shape.

   a   **b**

12 Part of a shape has been drawn with its two lines of symmetry.
Copy the diagram and draw the complete shape.

   a   **b**

17 C *Creating symmetrical patterns*

1 Look at the shape on the right.
Do you agree that it has a vertical line of symmetry ?

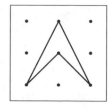

2 Make a copy of the grid on the right.
By joining the dots make three different shapes,
each of which has a vertical line of symmetry.

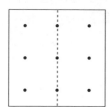

3 Make a copy of the grid on the right.
By joining the dots make three different shapes,
each of which has a horizontal line of symmetry.

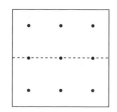

4 Make a copy of the grid on the right.
By joining the dots make three different shapes,
each of which has a diagonal line of symmetry.

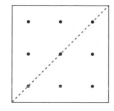

5 One of the shapes that you might have made in questions **2**, **3**
and **4** is shown on the right.
Do you agree that this shape has four lines of symmetry ?

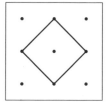

6 Look again at the shapes that you made in questions **2**, **3** and **4**.
  a Do any of the shapes you made have two lines of symmetry ?
  b Draw the shape again and mark on it both lines of symmetry.
  c Do any of the shapes you made have four lines of symmetry ?
  d Draw the shape again and mark on it all four lines of
    symmetry.

7 Look at the shape on the right.

   a Do you agree that it has four lines of symmetry ?

   b Make a copy of the shape and show the four lines of symmetry.

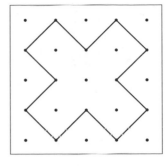

8 Make a copy of the grid on the right. By joining the dots make two different shapes which have:

   a only one line of symmetry

   b just two lines of symmetry

   c four lines of symmetry.

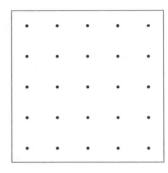

9 Fold a piece of paper in half. Cut out the shape shown opposite. Unfold the shape.

Does the shape have just one line of symmetry ?

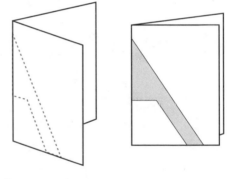

10 Fold a piece of paper in half twice. Cut out the shape shown opposite. Unfold the shape.

Does the shape have two lines of symmetry ?

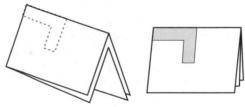

11 Which capital letters of the alphabet can you make by cutting out a shape from a piece of paper which has been:

   a folded once

   b folded twice ?

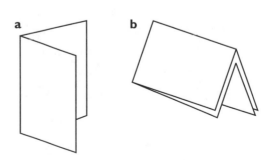

18 Solids

18 A Sorting and classifying three-dimensional shapes, corners, edges and faces

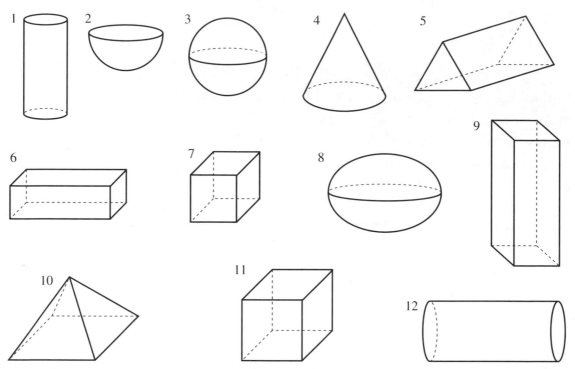

1 Which shapes above have faces which are:

  a flat only   **b** curved only   **c** both flat and curved ?

2 Which shapes above have 6 flat faces ? These are cuboids.

3 Which shapes above have 6 square faces ? These are cubes.

4 Which shapes above have 2 circular faces ? These are cylinders.

5 Join the shape with its name. The first is done for you.
(Copy the details first.)

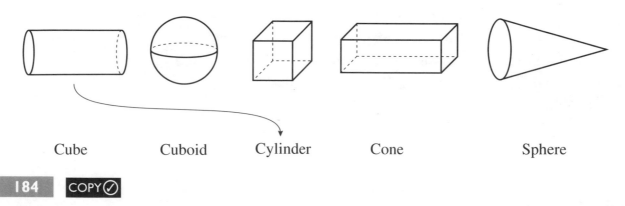

Cube   Cuboid   Cylinder   Cone   Sphere

COPY⊘

6 The shape on the right has six faces.

   a How many edges does this shape have ?

   b What shape are the faces ?

   c How many corners does this shape have ?

   d What do we call this shape ?

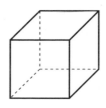

7 Look at the shape on the right.

   a How many faces does this shape have ?

   b What shape are these faces ?

   c How many edges does this shape have ?

   d How many corners does this shape have ?

   e What do we call this shape ?

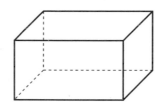

8 Look at the shape on the right.

   a How many faces does this shape have ?

   b What two shapes are the faces ?

   c How many edges does this shape have ?

   d How many corners does this shape have ?

This shape is called a triangular prism.

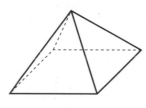

9 Look at the shape on the right.

   a How many faces does this shape have ?

   b What two shapes are the faces ?

   c How many edges does this shape have ?

   d How many corners does this shape have ?

This shape is called a pyramid.

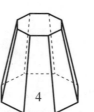

10

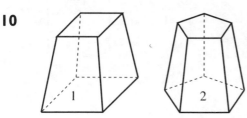

   a Copy and complete the table for the four shapes above. How are these results linked to the base of each solid ?

	Shape 1	Shape 2	Shape 3	Shape 4
Number of faces				
Number of edges				
Number of corners				

   b Check for each solid that:

Number of faces + Number of corners = Number of edges + 2

18 B *Recognising common three-dimensional shapes (cuboid, cylinder, cone, sphere)*

A **cube** has 6 faces each of which is an identical square.

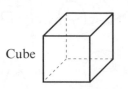

Cube

A **cuboid** has 6 faces. Its opposite faces are identical rectangles.

Cuboid

The **triangular prism** shown has a rectangular base, two identical triangular ends and two rectangular sloping sides.

Triangular prism

The **pyramid** shown has a square base and four identical triangular faces.

Pyramid

A **cylinder** has a two circular faces with the same radius and one curved face.

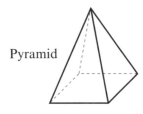

Cylinder

A **cone** has one flat circular face and one curved face.

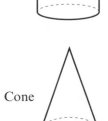

Cone

A **sphere** has a simple curved face.

Sphere

1 Look at the picture above.

   a How many cubes can you see ?

   b How many cuboids can you see ?

   c How many prisms can you see ?

   d How many pyramids can you see ?

   e How many cylinders can you see ?

   f How many cones can you see ?

   g How many spheres can you see ?

2 a Name two objects which are cubes in everyday life.
   (e.g. a sugar lump)

   b Name two objects which are cuboids in everyday life.

   c Name two objects which are prisms in everyday life.

   d Name two objects which are pyramids in everyday life.

   e Name two objects which are cylinders in everyday life.

   f Name two objects which are cones in everyday life.

   g Name two objects which are spheres in everyday life.

Three-dimensional shapes can be made from their nets.
The diagram shows the net of a cube.

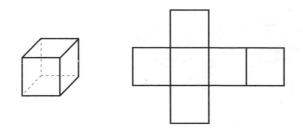

I Copy the net of a cube on a sheet of 1 cm squared graph paper
and construct the solid. Glue tabs are included.

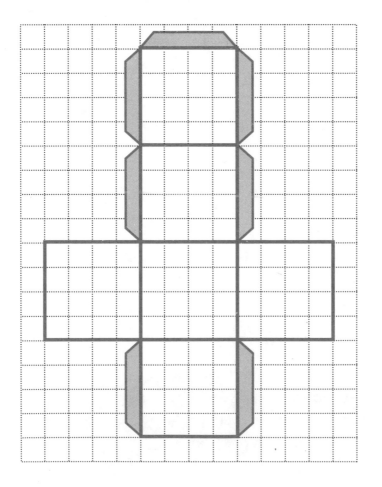

The diagram shows the net of a cuboid.

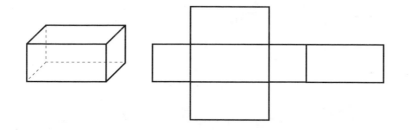

2 Copy the net of a cuboid on a sheet of 1 cm squared graph paper and construct the solid. Glue tabs are included.

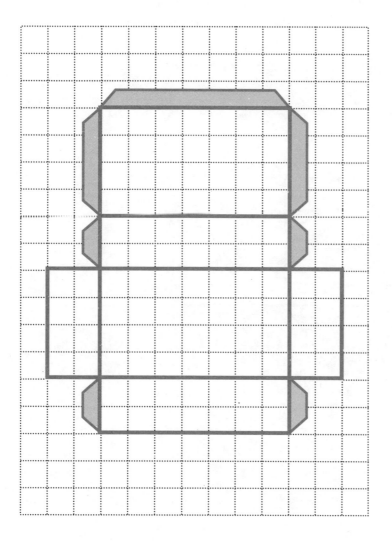

The diagram shows the net of a triangular prism.

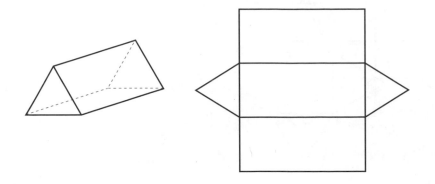

3 Copy the net of a triangular prism on a sheet of 1 cm squared graph paper and construct the solid. Glue tabs are included.

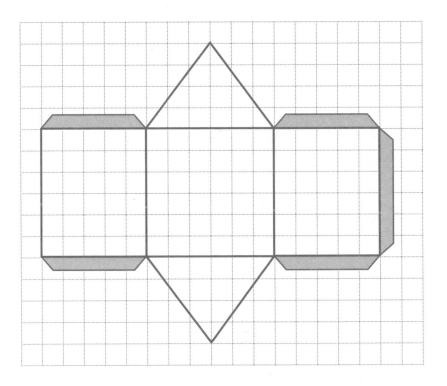

The diagram shows the net of a pyramid.

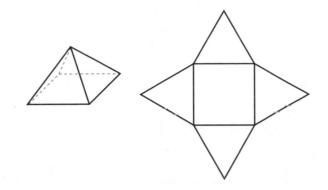

4 Copy the net of a pyramid on a sheet of 1 cm squared graph
paper and construct the solid. Glue tabs are included.

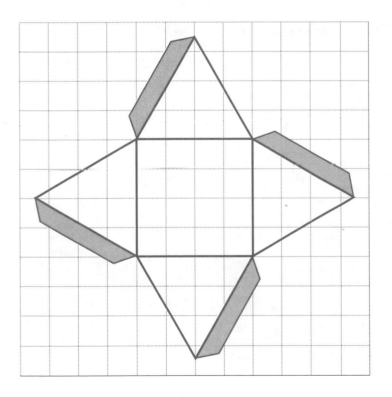

19   Position

19 A   Understanding the points of a compass

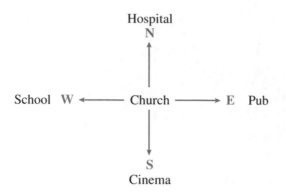

1   Look at the diagram above.
    Do you agree that the school is due West of the church ?

2 a   What place is due East of the church ?
  b   What place is due North of the church ?
  c   What place is due South of the church ?

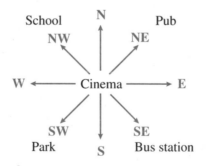

3   Look at the diagram above.
    Do you agree that the pub is NE of the cinema ?

4 a   What place is SE of the cinema ?
  b   What place is SW of the cinema ?
  c   What place is NW of the cinema ?

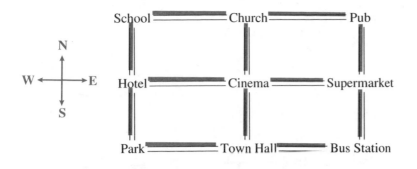

5 Look at the map above.
  a Do you agree that the cinema is due East of the hotel ?
  b What other place is also due East of the hotel ?

6 a What two places are due East of the school ?
  b What two places are due East of the park ?

7 a What two places are due North of the town hall ?
  b What two places are due North of the bus station ?

8 a What place is due South of the hotel ?
  b What place is due North of the hotel ?

9 a What place is due East of the church ?
  b What place is due West of the church ?

10 What is the direction of the cinema from the supermarket ?

11 a What place is NE of the cinema ?
  b What place is NW of the cinema ?

12 a What place is SE of the cinema ?
  b What place is SW of the cinema ?

19 B   *Identifying coordinates of points*

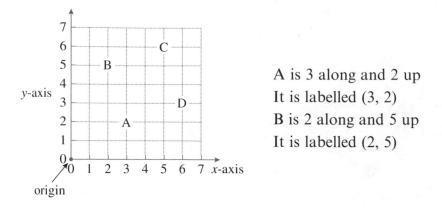

A is 3 along and 2 up
It is labelled (3, 2)
B is 2 along and 5 up
It is labelled (2, 5)

1 Look at the diagram above.

  a Do you agree that the point C can be labelled (5, 6) ?

  b Use coordinates to label the point D.

  c What shape is made if you join:

    A → B → C → D → A ?

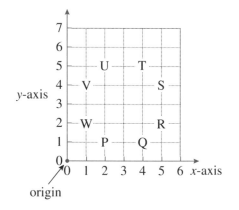

2 Look at the diagram above.

  a Do you agree that the coordinates of P are (2, 1) ?

  b Write down the coordinates of:

    i Q   **ii** R   **iii** S   **iv** T   **v** U   **vi** V   **vii** W

  c What shape is made if you join:

    P → Q → R → S → T → U → V → W → P ?

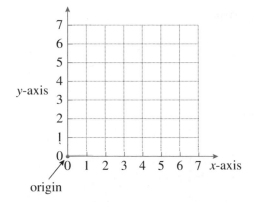

3 a On a copy of the grid above mark the points:

A (2, 1), B (4, 1), C (5, 3), D (4, 5), E (2, 5), F (1, 3)

b What shape is made if you join the points:

A → B → C → D → E → F → A ?

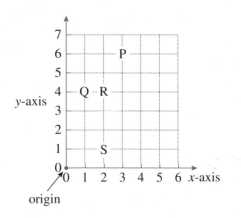

4 Look at the diagram above.

Write down the coordinates of:

a P **b** Q **c** R **d** S

5 a On a copy of the grid above mark the points:

T (4, 1), U (4, 4) and V (5, 4)

b Join the points:

P → Q → R → S → T → U → V → P

c What shape have you made ?

19 C *Drawing pictures using coordinates*

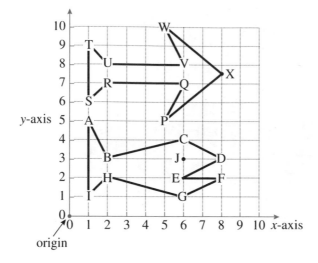

I Look at the diagram above.

    a Write down the coordinates of each point on the fish:
    A, B, C, D, E, F, G, H, I and J.

    b Write down the coordinates of each point on the arrow:
    P, Q, R, S, T, U, V, W and X.

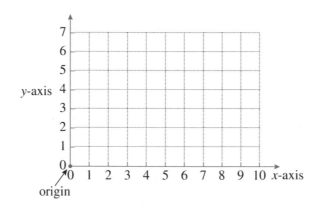

2 a On a copy of the diagram above mark the points whose
    coordinates are:

    A (2, 4),   B (3, 2),   C (9, 2),   D (10, 4),   E (7, 4),
    F (7, 5),   G (6, 5),   H (6, 6),   I (5, 6),   J (5, 5),
    K (4, 5),   L (4, 4)

    b Join the points in order. What shape have you made ?

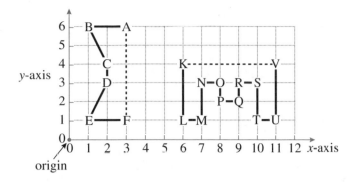

3 Look at the diagram above.

Write down the coordinates of the points: A, B, C, D, E, and F.

4 a On a copy of the diagram above draw the other half of the shape for which the line AF is a line of symmetry.

b Write down the coordinates of the other four points on the complete shape.

5 Look again at the diagram above.

Write down the coordinates of the points:

K, L, M, N, O, P, Q, R, S, T, U and V.

6 a On a copy of the diagram above draw the other half of the shape for which the line KV is a line of symmetry.

b Write down the coordinates of the other ten points on the complete shape.

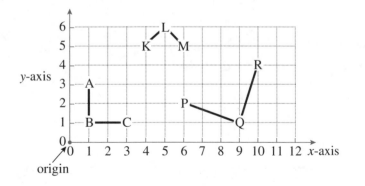

7 Look at the diagram above.

ABCD, KLMN and PQRS are all squares.

Write down the coordinates of the points:

a D   **b** N   **c** S

20 Reading data

20 A Extracting information from lists

Traffic surveys are often carried out at junctions and roundabouts to collect data so that design can be improved to minimise delays. Car manufacturers also use the information on the make of car, body shape (saloon, hatchback or estate), colour, number of doors and number of occupants. The data from a survey is shown below.

	Make of car	Body shape (S, H or E)	Colour	Doors	Number of occupants
1	Rover	S	red	4	1
2	Nissan	H	red	4	1
3	Ford	E	blue	4	5
4	Volvo	E	blue	4	1
5	Rover	H	green	4	1
6	Rover	H	blue	4	1
7	Nissan	S	red	4	4
8	Rover	S	green	2	1
9	Nissan	S	white	2	1
10	Ford	H	white	2	2

For questions **1** to **5** you will need the information in the above table.

1 Write down the number of cars made by:
   a Ford   **b** Nissan   **c** Volvo   **d** Rover.

2 Write down the number of cars which are:
   a estates   **b** hatchbacks   **c** saloons.

3 Write down the number of cars which are:
   a blue   **b** green   **c** white   **d** red.

4 Write down the number of cars with:
   a 2 doors   **b** 4 doors.

5 Write down the number of cars with:
   a 1 occupant   **b** 2 occupants   **c** 4 occupants   **d** 5 occupants.

Fifteen children on a school excursion each bought a sandwich, a packet of crisps and a drink from a set of vending machines. Their choices are shown in the table below.

	Name	Filling (sandwich)	Flavour (crisps)	Drink
1	Sally	Cheese	Plain	Coffee
2	Kate	Ham	Cheese and onion	Lemonade
3	Janet	Egg	Bovril	Orange squash
4	Jodie	Cheese	Cheese and onion	Coffee
5	Elaine	Egg	Cheese and onion	Lemonade
6	Sharon	Tomato	Plain	Orange squash
7	Samantha	Ham	Cheese and onion	Tea
8	Mumbi	Cheese	Plain	Lemonade
9	Peter	Egg	Cheese and onion	Lemonade
10	Matthew	Ham	Cheese and onion	Coffee
11	Bradley	Egg	Bovril	Lemonade
12	Adam	Tomato	Plain	Orange squash
13	Richard	Egg	Salt and vinegar	Coffee
14	Sanjay	Cheese	Plain	Lemonade
15	Sunil	Egg	Cheese and onion	Coffee

For questions **6** to **8** you will need the information in the above table.

6 Write down the number of sandwich fillings which are:

   a cheese   **b** ham   **c** egg   **d** tomato.

7 Write down the number of crisps which are:

   a plain   **b** Bovril   **c** salt and vinegar   **d** cheese and onion.

8 Write down the number of drinks which are:

   a tea   **b** coffee   **c** lemonade   **d** orange squash.

9 The heights in cm of the fifteen children above are:

   146, 152, 137, 142, 159, 143, 154, 155, 161, 129, 138, 142, 149, 153, 158.

   a Write the list of heights in ascending order (i.e. 129, 137, 138, ...).

   b Find the number of heights in each of the groups below:

     i 120–129 cm **ii** 130–139 cm **iii** 140–149 cm **iv** 150–159 cm

1 The pictogram on the right shows the number
of cars of different makes in a survey.
How many cars are made by:
  a Ford
  b Nissan
  c Rover
  d Volvo ?

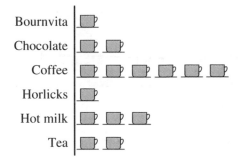

2 The favourite drink of each of fifteen children
is shown in the pictogram on the right.
How many children chose:
  a Bournvita
  b chocolate
  c coffee
  d Horlicks
  e hot milk
  f tea ?

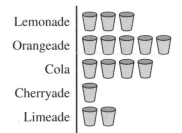

3 The pictogram shows how many fizzy drinks of
different flavours were dispensed by a vending
machine on a certain day.
If each symbol stands for 10 drinks, find:
  a the number of drinks of each flavour which were
  dispensed
  b the total number of drinks dispensed altogether.

4 The pictogram shows how many packets of
crisps of different flavours were dispensed by
a vending machine on a certain day. If each
symbol stands for 10 packets of crisps, find:
  a the number of packets of each flavour which
  were dispensed
  b the total number of packets dispensed altogether.

5 The pictogram shows how much money was raised for two different charities. If each symbol represents £100, find how much each charity received.

6 The pictogram shows how many cut-price CDs a shop sold on each day of a certain week. If each symbol stands for 10 CDs find:

a the number of CDs sold on each day of the week

b the total number of CDs sold altogether.

If each CD cost £5, find:

c the total amount of money spent.

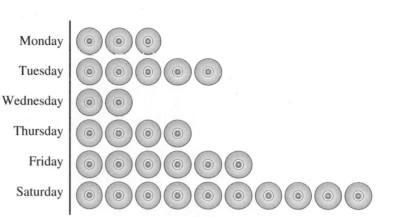

7 The pictogram shows how many letters a firm sent out on each day of a certain week. If each symbol stands for 10 letters, find:

a the number of letters sent out on each day of the week

b the total number of letters sent out altogether.

If the stamp for each letter costs 20p, find:

c the total amount spent on postage.

8 The pictogram shows how many cornets an ice cream man sold each month during the summer season. If each symbol stands for 100 cornets, find:

a the number of cornets sold each month

b the total number of cornets sold altogether.

If each cornet costs 80p, find:

c the ice cream seller's total sales.

20 C   *Reading bar charts*

I The bar chart on the right shows the number of cars of different makes in a survey.

How many cars are made by:

a Ford

b Nissan

c Rover

d Volvo ?

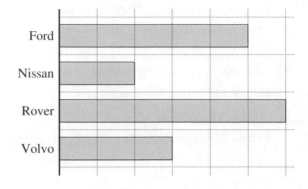

2 The favourite drink of each of twenty children is shown in the bar chart on the right.

How many children chose:

a Bournvita

b chocolate

c coffee

d Horlicks

e hot milk

f tea ?

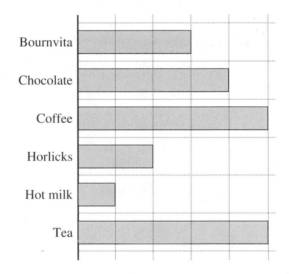

3 The bar chart shows how many fizzy drinks of different flavours were dispensed by a vending machine on a certain day.

If each square stands for 5 drinks find:

a the number of drinks of each flavour which were dispensed

b the total number of drinks dispensed altogether.

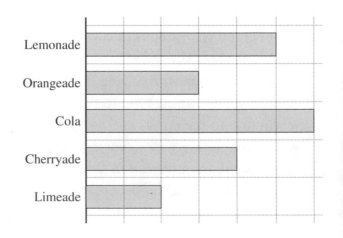

4 The bar chart shows how many letters a firm sent out on each day of a certain week. If each square stands for 10 letters, find:

  a the number of letters sent out on each day of the week

  b the total number of letters sent out altogether.

If the stamp for each letter costs 20p, find:

  c the total amount spent on postage.

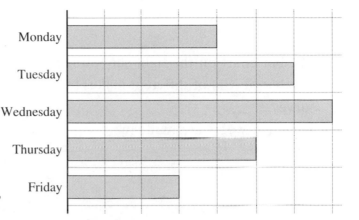

5 The bar chart shows how many barges passed through a set of lock gates on a canal on each day of a certain week. If one square represents 5 barges, find:

  a the number that passed through on each day of the week

  b the total number that passed through altogether.

If each lock takes 4 minutes to fill, find:

  c the total time that the lock was operating.

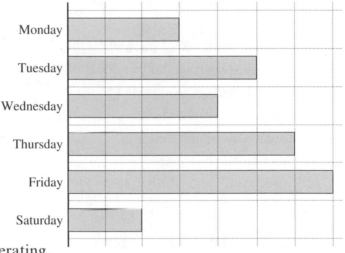

6 The bar chart shows how many pupils there are in each of the five years in a secondary school. If each square represents 20 pupils, find:

  a the number of pupils in each year

  b the total number of pupils in the school altogether.

One day the whole school went on an excursion to the coast.

If the coach fare was £8 each, find:

  c the total amount paid in fares.

If they hired 60-seater coaches, find:

  d the total number of coaches needed.

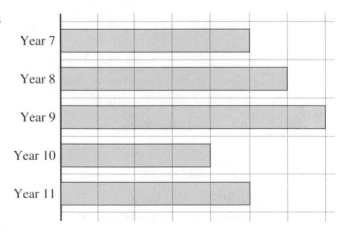

21 Displaying data

21 A Completing tally charts

1 Fifteen children were asked their favourite drink from: Bournvita, chocolate, coffee, Horlicks, hot milk and tea.
Their answers are shown below.

Anne	tea	Adam	Horlicks	David	coffee
Emma	coffee	Fran	hot milk	George	tea
Miranda	tea	Razi	chocolate	Salik	hot milk
Zorba	coffee	Azil	hot milk	Melissa	Bournvita
Paul	coffee	Satwinder	chocolate	Yusuf	Horlicks

a Copy and complete the tally chart shown on the right. The first two entries have been done for you.

b What is the most popular drink ?

c How many of the children chose coffee ?

Drink	Tally	Total
Bournvita	l	1
chocolate	ll	2
coffee		
Horlicks		
hot milk		
tea		
	Total tally	15

2 The same fifteen children, who were all born in 1990, were asked their month and date of birth.
Their answers are shown below.

Anne	1 July	Adam	1 May	David	7 January
Emma	9 June	Fran	7 July	George	1 January
Miranda	12 October	Razi	1 December	Salik	9 April
Zorba	1 March	Azil	7 November	Melissa	14 July
Paul	12 December	Satwinder	1 February	Yusuf	4 January

a Copy and complete the tally chart shown on the right.

b What is the most common date of the month ?

c How many of the children had a birthday on the 7th ?

d Make up a similar tally chart to show how often a particular month occurred as a birthday.

Date of month	Tally	Total
1	lЖ l	6
4	l	1
7		
9		
12		
14		
	Total tally	15

COPY ⊘

3 The children at High Lane school had an excursion day with five excursions to choose from. Their choices are as shown below.

Name	Place	Name	Place
Mary	London Zoo	Jane	Brighton
Vepula	Portsmouth	Mumbi	Thorpe Park
Gillian	Portsmouth	Sunil	North Downs
Nishil	Thorpe Park	Derek	Brighton
Geoffrey	Portsmouth	Matthew	Brighton
Janet	Thorpe Park	Melissa	North Downs
Natalie	Portsmouth	Rosie	Brighton
Naomi	Thorpe Park	Sanjay	London Zoo
Asif	Brighton	John	Thorpe Park
Chris	North Downs	Peter	Thorpe Park

a Construct a tally chart to show the above information.

b Which was the most popular choice of excursion ?

4 The heights of fifteen children are shown below.

Anne	127 cm	Adam	136 cm	David	158 cm
Emma	147 cm	Fran	142 cm	George	111 cm
Miranda	125 cm	Razi	116 cm	Salik	148 cm
Zorba	151 cm	Azil	119 cm	Melissa	120 cm
Paul	145 cm	Satwinder	128 cm	Yusuf	149 cm

a Copy and complete the tally chart shown on the right.

b What is the most common group of heights ?

c How many of the children have heights between 120 cm and 129 cm ?

Height	Tally	Total
110–119 cm	|||	3
120–129 cm		
130–139 cm		
140–149 cm		
150–159 cm		
	Total tally	15

5 The weights of twenty children are shown below.

Anne	42 kg	Adam	27 kg	David	47 kg	Tom	57 kg
Emma	28 kg	Fran	33 kg	George	34 kg	Ian	51 kg
Miranda	32 kg	Razi	44 kg	Salik	55 kg	Rita	53 kg
Zorba	48 kg	Azil	35 kg	Melissa	39 kg	Mary	43 kg
Paul	45 kg	John	46 kg	Yusuf	38 kg	Lynn	41 kg

Construct a tally chart to show how many of the above weights are in each of the groups: 20–29 kg, 30–39 kg, 40–49 kg, 50–59 kg.

 205

21 B   *Creating frequency tables*

1 The results of a survey of the colours of ten cars are shown below.

Rover Citroen	red blue	Nissan Peugeot	red white	Ford Fiat	blue red	Vauxhall Honda	white red	Volvo Jaguar	white green

a Copy and complete the frequency table started below:

Colour	Blue	Green	Red	White
Frequency	2			

b Which colour was the most frequent in the above survey ?

2 Twelve boys chose their sports options as shown below.

Julian	rugby	Ronnie	football	Wayne	football
Martyn	cross country	Ayo	hockey	Jisanne	rugby
Josiah	hockey	Marlon	cross country	Jordan	football
Marcus	rugby	George	cross country	Bernard	football

a Copy and complete the frequency table started below:

Sports option	Cross country	Football	Hockey	Rugby
Frequency	3			

b Which sport was the most popular choice in the above survey ?

3 Fifteen girls chose their sports options as shown below.

Jean	netball	Shani	lacrosse	Diane	tennis
Barbara	hockey	Tnisha	hockey	Laura	netball
Rita	hockey	Anne	netball	Patricia	hockey
Suzanne	lacrosse	Margaret	netball	Gillian	netball
Candace	netball	Nicola	lacrosse	Jane	tennis

a Copy and complete the frequency table below:

Sports option	Hockey	Lacrosse	Netball	Tennis
Frequency				

b Which sport was the most popular choice in the above survey ?

4 Fifteen girls chose their favourite drink as shown below.

Jean	coffee	Shani	orangeade	Diane	coffee
Barbara	lemonade	Tnisha	tea	Laura	tea
Rita	orangeade	Anne	lemonade	Patricia	coffee
Suzanne	coffee	Margaret	lemonade	Gillian	coffee
Candace	lemonade	Nicola	coffee	Jane	lemonade

Construct a frequency table to show the above choices.

5 The heights and weights of twenty children are shown below.

Child	Height (cm)	Weight (kg)	Child	Height (cm)	Weight (kg)
1	146	42	11	138	37
2	152	46	12	142	46
3	137	39	13	149	42
4	142	41	14	153	45
5	159	51	15	158	51
6	143	47	16	142	47
7	154	43	17	147	43
8	155	48	18	135	38
9	120	29	19	146	45
10	129	35	20	158	53

a Write down the heights in ascending order (lowest first).

b Copy and complete the frequency table started below.

Height	120–129 cm	130–139 cm	140–149 cm	150–159 cm
Frequency	2			

c Which was the most common group of heights ?

d Write down the weights in ascending order (lowest first).

e Copy and complete the frequency table started below.

Weight	20–29 kg	30–39 kg	40–49 kg	50–59 kg
Frequency	1			

f Which was the most common group of weights ?

6 Eighteen children took part in an archery contest where they shot three arrows each. Their scores were as follows:

Derek	11	Leslie	13	Judith	14
Carl	6	Brian	25	Lorraine	23
Sunil	1	William	8	Candace	15
Sanjay	19	Shani	18	Laura	13
Raymond	12	Joanna	11	Mumbi	3
Nishil	21	Elaine	16	Wambui	9

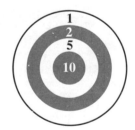

a Write down the above scores in ascending order (lowest first).

b Copy and complete the frequency table started below.

Score	0–9	10–19	20–29
Frequency	5		

c Copy and complete the frequency table started below.

Score	0–4	5–9	10–14	15–19	20–24	25–29
Frequency	2					

1 The results of a survey of numbers of different makes of cars
were:

Fiat	1	Ford	8
Honda	2	Nissan	3
Rover	6	Volvo	2

Draw a pictogram using the symbol illustrated.

2 The results of a survey of numbers of different makes of beer
were:

Ansels	1	Flowers	1
Boddingtons	5	Grolsh	4
Carlsberg	3	Strongs	2

Draw a pictogram using the symbol illustrated.

3 The numbers of parcels posted by a firm on each day of a week
are:

Monday	2	Thursday	6
Tuesday	3	Friday	7
Wednesday	5	Saturday	1

Draw a pictogram using the symbol illustrated.

4 A newspaper boy delivers magazines to Read Street in
Papertown.
Draw a pictogram using the symbol illustrated.

Monday	5	Wednesday	5	Friday	6	Sunday	7
Tuesday	5	Thursday	5	Saturday	8		

5 The numbers of letters posted by a firm on each day of a week are:

Monday	20	Thursday	60
Tuesday	30	Friday	70
Wednesday	50	Saturday	10

Draw a pictogram using the symbol illustrated.
(**Note**: each envelope is used to represent ten letters.)

6 The numbers of bottles delivered by a milkman each day are:

Monday	30	Thursday	40
Tuesday	40	Friday	50
Wednesday	40	Saturday	90

Draw a pictogram using the symbol illustrated.
(**Note**: each bottle is used to represent ten bottles of milk.)

7 The numbers of ice creams sold by a shop on each day of a week are:

Monday	5	Thursday	30
Tuesday	10	Friday	25
Wednesday	20	Saturday	40

Draw a pictogram using the symbol illustrated.
(**Note**: each cornet is used to represent five ice creams.)

8 The numbers of points scored by a rugby team in five matches are:

Match 1	40	Match 4	60
Match 2	20	Match 5	30
Match 3	20		

Draw a pictogram using the symbol illustrated.
(**Note**: 1 ball represents 10 points.)

21 D *Constructing bar charts and block graphs*

1 The results of a survey of numbers of different makes of cars were:

Fiat	2	Ford	6
Honda	1	Nissan	4
Rover	4	Volvo	3

Display these details on a bar chart.

2 The results of a survey of numbers of different makes of beer were:

Ansels	2	Flowers	2
Boddingtons	3	Grolsh	5
Carlsberg	4	Strongs	1

Display these details on a bar chart.

3 The numbers of parcels posted by a firm on each day of a week are:

Monday	1	Thursday	8
Tuesday	2	Friday	5
Wednesday	4	Saturday	1

Display these details on a bar chart.

4 A newspaper boy delivers magazines to Read Street in Papertown.
Construct a bar chart to show how many he delivers each day.

Monday	2	Wednesday	5	Friday	6	Sunday	4
Tuesday	3	Thursday	1	Saturday	7		

5 The block graph on the right shows the number of people who bought different drinks in a cafe on a Sunday afternoon.

a Do you agree that three people drank chocolate in the cafe ?

b Do you agree that one person had a milk shake ?

c How many people drank:
  i coffee   **ii** orange juice
  iii tea ?

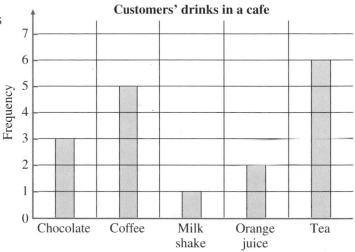

6 Draw a block graph like the one above to show how many cars were sold on each day of the week at the Super Auto Garage.

| Monday | 5 | Wednesday | 5 | Friday | 1 |
| Tuesday | 2 | Thursday | 4 | Saturday | 8 |

7 The block graph on the right shows the heights of twelve children.

a Do you agree that there are five children with heights between 110 cm and 119 cm ?

b How many children are of height:
  i 120–129 cm   **ii** 130–139 cm ?

c How would the graph alter to show another child of height 125 cm ?

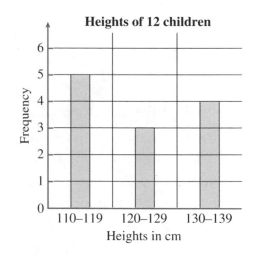

8 The weights of the twelve children in question **7** are listed below. Draw a block graph like the one above to show these weights.

  20–29 kg: 2,   30–39 kg: 5,   40–49 kg: 3,   50–59 kg: 2

21 E Constructing line graphs

1 A patient in hospital had his temperature taken at hourly intervals.

The readings between 6 a.m. and 12 noon are shown below.

Time	6 a.m.	7 a.m.	8 a.m.	9 a.m.	10 a.m.	11 a.m.	12 noon
Temperature	35·7°C	35·3°C	35·4°C	36·0°C	36·4°C	37·0°C	36·4°C

Look at the bar line graph which has been started on the right.

a Do you agree that at 6 a.m. it shows a temperature of 35·7°C?

b What temperature is shown at:
   i 7 a.m.   **ii** 8 a.m.   **iii** 9 a.m. ?

c Copy this bar line graph and complete it to show, for the table above, the temperatures at:
   i 10 a.m.   **ii** 11 a.m.   **iii** 12 noon.

d Estimate the patient's temperature at:
   i 6.30 a.m.   **ii** 9.30 a.m.

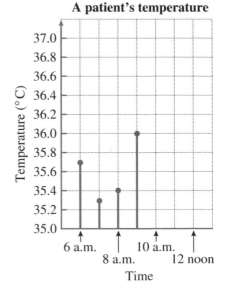

A patient's temperature

2 Look at the line graph which has been started on the right.

a Do you agree that at 9 a.m. it shows a temperature of 36·0°C?

b What temperature is shown at:
   i 10 a.m.   **ii** 11 a.m.   **iii** 12 noon ?

c Copy this line graph and complete it to show, for the table above, the temperatures at:
   i 6 a.m.   **ii** 7 a.m.   **iii** 8 a.m.

d Estimate the patient's temperature at:
   i 8.30 a.m.   **ii** 10.30 a.m.

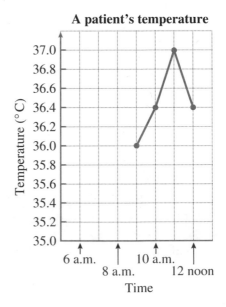

A patient's temperature

3 Mary was born in 1988. Her mother decided to record her weight.
The bar line graph below shows her weight at two-year intervals.

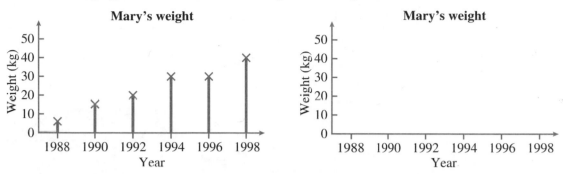

a Copy the table below. Use the bar line graph to complete it.

Year	1988	1990	1992	1994	1996	1998
Weight (kg)						

b Copy the grid on the right above.
Use your completed table in **a** to draw a line graph.

c Use your graph in **b** to find Mary's weight in:
  i 1989   **ii** 1997.

4 An immersion heater is turned on at 8 a.m. and turned off at 3 p.m. The bar line graph on the right shows the temperature at hourly intervals.

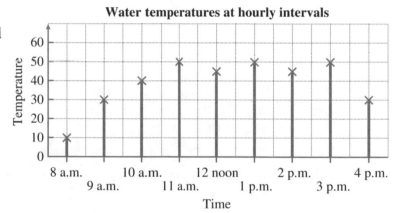

Water temperatures at hourly intervals

a Copy the table below. Use the bar line graph to complete it.

Time (hourly)	8 a.m.	9 a.m.	10 a.m.	11 a.m.	12 noon	1 p.m.	2 p.m.	3 p.m.	4 p.m.
Temperature (°C)									

b Copy the grid above without the vertical bars.
Use your completed table in **a** to draw a line graph.

c Use your graph in **b** to find the temperature at:
  i 8.30 a.m.   **ii** 9.30 a.m.   **iii** 10.30 a.m.   **iv** 3.30 p.m.

d Why does the temperature oscillate between 11 a.m. and 3 p.m. ?

21 F   Using diagrams

1 Look at the diagram on the right. It shows a set of
shapes and a loop in which we place the triangles.
On a copy of the diagram show where each of the
following shapes should be placed.

a

b

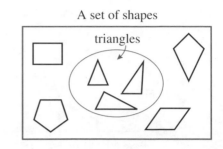

A set of shapes

triangles

2 Look at the diagram on the right. It shows a set of
shapes and a loop in which we place the quadrilaterals.
On a copy of the diagram show where each of the
following shapes should be placed.

a

b

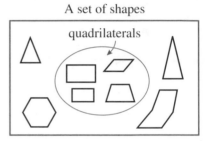

A set of shapes

quadrilaterals

3 Look at the diagram on the right. It shows a set of
numbers and a loop in which we place the multiples
of three. On a copy of the diagram show where each
of the following numbers should be placed.

 a 4   **b** 7   **c** 9   **d** 11

Whole numbers from 1 to 12

multiples of three

1   2   3   5

6

12   8

10

4 Look at the diagram on the right. It shows a set of
numbers and a loop in which we place the multiples
of five. On a copy of the diagram show where each
of the following numbers should be placed.

 a 4   **b** 15   **c** 16   **d** 20

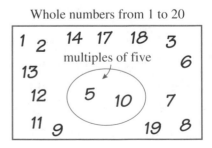

Whole numbers from 1 to 20

1   2   14   17   18   3

13   multiples of five   6

12   5   10   7

11   9   19   8

COPY ✓

5 The diagram on the right shows a set of
shapes together with two overlapping loops.
One loop is for black shapes, the other
loop is for triangles.

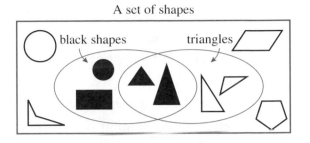

A set of shapes

a Do you agree that the only shapes which
can be placed in the centre region are
shapes which are black triangles ?

b Do you agree that the only shapes which can be placed in the
outer region are shapes which are neither black nor triangles ?

c On a copy of the diagram above show where each of the
following shapes should be placed.

i    ii 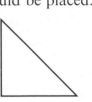   iii    iv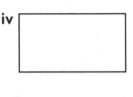

6 The diagram on the right shows a set of
numbers with two overlapping loops.
One loop is for even numbers, the other
loop is for multiples of three.

whole numbers from 1 to 20

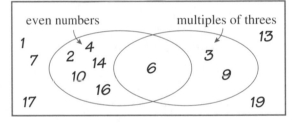

a Do you agree that the only numbers
which can be placed in the centre
region are numbers which are even
multiples of three ?

b Do you agree that the only numbers which can be placed in the
outer region are numbers which are neither even numbers nor
numbers which are multiples of three ?

c On a copy of the diagram above show where each of the
following numbers should be placed.

i 5   **ii** 8   **iii** 9   **iv** 11   **v** 12   **vi** 15   **vii** 18   **viii** 20

22 Interpreting data

22 A Interpreting frequency diagrams

1 The block graph on the right shows the frequency (i.e. how many) of different makes of car in a survey.

  a Do you agree that the number of Ford cars shown is 3 ?

  b How many of the cars shown were made by:

    i Nissan   **ii** Rover   **iii** Volvo ?

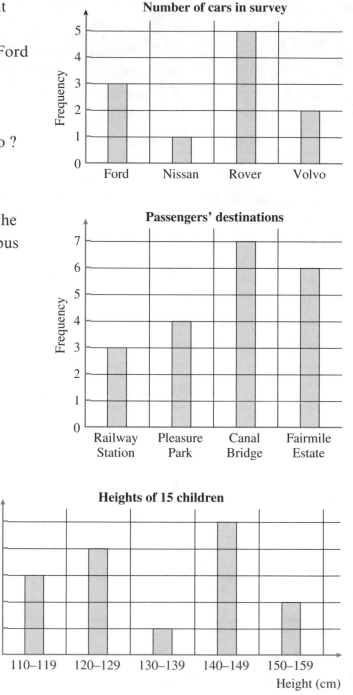

2 The block graph on the right shows the frequency of destinations on a local bus service.

How many people got off at:

  a the Railway Station

  b the Pleasure Park

  c the Canal Bridge

  d the Fairmile Estate ?

3 The block graph on the right shows the frequency of heights of 15 children in a youth club. How many children's heights are in the group:

  a 110–119 cm

  b 120–129 cm

  c 130–139 cm

  d 140–149 cm

  e 150–159 cm ?

4 The block graph on the right shows how many people paid for their travel on a local bus service by different methods.

How many people used:

a an OAP pass

b a season ticket

c a school pass ?

What method of payment was:

d the most common

e the least common ?

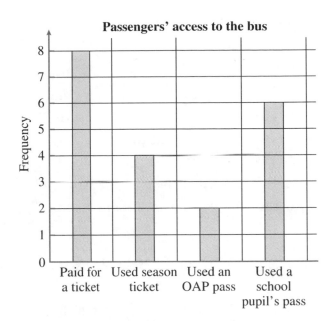

Passengers' access to the bus

5 The block graph on the right shows the numbers of first-class passengers on different trains.

a Do you agree that there were 3 trains which carried between 40 and 49 first-class passengers ?

b Which numbers of first-class passengers were most common ? How many trains carried these numbers ?

c Which numbers of first-class passengers was least common ?

d How many trains carried these numbers ?

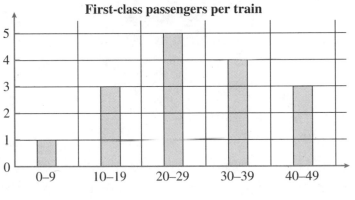

First-class passengers per train

22 B *Interpreting pie charts*

1 The pie chart on the right shows the makes of 40 cars in a survey.

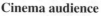

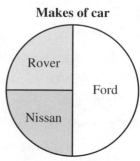

Makes of car

  a Do you agree that this shows that half of the cars are Fords ?
  b How many of the cars are Fords ?
  c Do you agree that this shows that one quarter of the cars are Rovers ?
  d How many of the cars are Rovers ?
  e How many of the cars are Nissans ?

2 The pie chart on the right shows a survey of 60 people in a cinema.

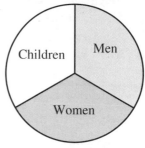

Cinema audience

  a Do you agree that this shows that one third of the people are men ?
  b How many women are there ?
  c How many children are there ?

3 The pie chart shows how 24 pupils in Class 8A travel to school.

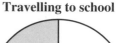

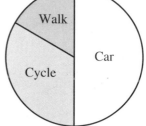

Travelling to school

  a How many pupils travel by car ?
  b Do you agree that one third of the pupils cycle to school ?
  c How many pupils cycle to school ?
  d Do you agree that one sixth of the pupils walk to school ?
  e How many pupils walk to school ?

4 The pie chart shows how all 120 girls in Year 12 chose their sports option.

Sports options

  a Which was the most popular sport ?
  b Which were the least popular sports ?
  c What fraction of the pie chart is used to represent those who chose:
  i netball   **ii** hockey   **iii** squash ?
  d How many girls chose:
  i netball   **ii** hockey   **iii** squash ?

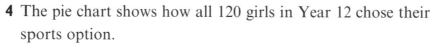

5 The pie chart on the right shows how a total of 36 goals were scored by three football teams.

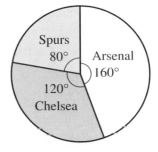

   a As the total angle of 360° is used to represent the 36 goals, do you agree that each 10° will represent one goal ?

   b How many goals were scored by:
     i Arsenal   **ii** Chelsea   **iii** Spurs ?

6 One week a car dealer sold 180 cars. The pie chart shows how many were sold on each day of the week.

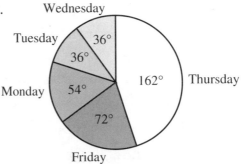

   a On which day were most sold ?

   b On which days were least sold ?

   c Do you agree that each 2° in the pie chart represents one car ?

   d How many cars were sold on:
     i Monday   **ii** Tuesday   **iii** Friday ?

(**Note**: 360 = 2 × 180)

7 One week a shop sold 90 packets of crisps. The pie chart shows how many of each flavour were sold that week.

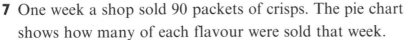
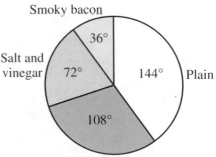

   a Which flavour was most popular ?

   b Which flavour was least popular ?

   c Do you agree that each 4° in the pie chart represents one packet ?

   d How many of the packets sold were:
     i smoky bacon   **ii** salt and vinegar
     iii cheese and onion   **iv** plain ?

(**Note**: 360 = 4 × 90)

8 The pie chart shows how all 360 boys in Year 10 chose their sports option.

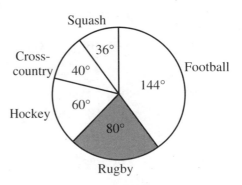
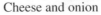

   a Which was the most popular sport ?

   b Which was the least popular sport ?

   c How many boys chose:
     i cross-country   **ii** hockey   **iii** rugby ?

22 c *Finding the mode and the median of a set of data*

The **mode** of a set is the number (or quantity) which occurs most
often in the set.

1 A primary school has ten classes.
   The number of pupils in each of the classes is as follows:
   16, 16, 17, 18, 18, 18, 18, 19, 20 and 20.
   a What number occurs most often in the above list ?
   b Do you agree that 18 is the mode of this set of class sizes ?

2 Laura travels to school by bus.
   Over a two-week period her journey times are:
   31, 32, 32, 33, 33, 33, 33, 34, 34 and 34 minutes.
   a What time occurs most often in the above list ?
   b Do you agree that 33 minutes is the mode of this set of journey
   times ?

3 Twelve taxis departed from a rank and the passenger numbers
   were:
   4, 3, 1, 5, 2, 4, 5, 4, 2, 5, 1 and 5.
   a Write the above list in order starting with the smallest
   (i.e. 1, 1, 2, 2, 3, . . .).
   b What number occurs most often in the above list ?
   c What is the mode of this set of numbers ?

4 Clare travels to work by train on Mondays to Saturdays. She
   recorded how late her train was over a two-week period:
   2, 3, 0, 1, 4, 0, 1, 3, 2, 1, 0 and 1 minutes.
   a Write the above list in order starting with the smallest time.
   b What time occurs most often in the above list ?
   c What is the mode of this set of times ?

5 John is a train spotter. One day he noticed that nine trains
   departed from a station during the evening peak hour.
   He recorded the number of coaches that each train had:
   6, 8, 4, 12, 4, 6, 4, 12 and 8.
   a Find the number that occurs most often in the above list.
   b What is the modal number of coaches ?

The **median** of a set is the middle number (or quantity) of the set when it is arranged in ascending order.

6 Mary counted the number of sweets in each of five similar packets. The numbers were: 22, 23, 24, 26 and 27.
   a What is the middle number of the list ?
   b Do you agree that the median of this set of numbers is 24 ?

7 Mrs. Brown has five children. Their weights are:
   51 kg, 39 kg, 48 kg, 53 kg and 42 kg.
   a Write the above list in order starting with the smallest weight.
   b What is the middle weight of your rearranged list ?
   c Do you agree that the median of this set of weights is 48 kg ?

8 One week the attendance figures for Class 8A were:
   21, 18, 17, 20 and 19.
   a Write the above list in order starting with the smallest.
   b What is the middle number of your rearranged list ?
   c What is the median of this set of numbers ?

9 The distances between successive locks along a canal are:
   500, 300, 900, 650, 600, 400, 750, 450 and 800 metres.
   a Write the above list in order starting with the smallest distance.
   b What is the median of this set of numbers ?

Note: When there is an **even** number of items in the set the median is taken to be the number **half-way** between the two middle numbers.

10 What is the median of this set of numbers: 2, 3, 4, 6, 7 and 9 ?

11 The heights of Susan and nine of her friends are listed below:
   120, 116, 117, 113, 122, 114, 121, 124, 112 and 119 cm
   a Write the above list in order starting with the smallest height.
   b What is the median of this set of heights ?

12 The prices of fish and chips in eight different shops were:
   £2.00, £2.30, £2.70, £2.10, £2.40, £2.45, £2.25, £2.75
   Find the median of this set of prices.

23 Surveys

23 A Collecting and displaying data

1 A survey of sixteen people employed in a cafe is shown below.

Employee	Working capacity	Rest day	Employee	Working capacity	Rest day
Vepula	Waitress	Monday	Sheila	Dish washer	Tuesday
Wambui	Cook	Thursday	Lesley	Waitress	Saturday
Patricia	Waitress	Thursday	Jimmy	Cook	Tuesday
Julie	Cleaner	Monday	Peter	Cashier	Monday
Jane	Waitress	Friday	Tom	Dish washer	Thursday
Dawn	Cook	Sunday	Anish	Cleaner	Tuesday
Valerie	Cleaner	Wednesday	Andrew	Dish washer	Monday
Barbara	Cashier	Tuesday	Michael	Cook	Friday

a Make out a tally chart which shows how many workers are:

   i employed in each of the five capacities

   ii off work on each of the days of the week.

b Show each set of information in **a** as a bar chart.

c On which days of the week are most of the employees off work ?

d On which days of the week are most of the employees at work ?

2 Coaches leave a coach station for four different resorts.

A survey of the departures between 0800 and 1000 is shown below.

Departure time	Destination	Seating capacity	Departure time	Destination	Seating capacity
0800	Hastings	50	0900	Hastings	50
0805	Brighton	45	0905	Southend	60
0810	Southend	55	0910	Bournemouth	50
0815	Bournemouth	50	0920	Brighton	55
0825	Bournemouth	60	0930	Hastings	45
0830	Brighton	50	0935	Bournemouth	60
0840	Southend	45	0945	Brighton	50

a Make out a tally chart which shows how many coaches:

   i went to each of the four destinations

   ii had each of the four different seating capacities.

b Show each set of information in **a** as a bar chart.

c To which resorts could 60 people travel on the same coach ?

3 A survey was carried out of the highest mark scored by each of 24 pupils in a set of exams. The marks out of 100 are shown below.

Name	Mark	Name	Mark	Name	Mark
Lynn	41	Shani	61	David	36
Sheila	56	Rita	78	Michael	65
Margaret	35	Mary	67	Geoffrey	28
Dawn	63	Frances	75	Tom	71
Susan	24	Peter	51	Daniel	45
Lisa	25	Andrew	32	Ian	58
Natalie	57	Paul	52	Robert	46
Candace	48	John	75	Tnisha	54

a Arrange the above marks in ascending order (lowest first).

b What is the middle (median) mark in the above set of marks ?

c Copy and complete the frequency chart shown below:

Mark	20–29	30–39	40–49	50–59	60–69	70–79
Frequency						

d Using your results in **c** above copy and complete the block graph shown below.

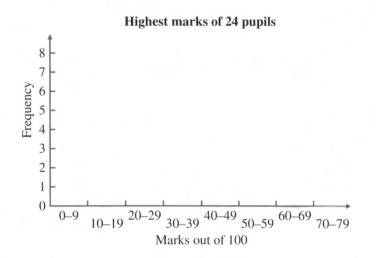

e Which range of marks contains the largest number of pupils ?

f Which ranges of marks contains the smallest number of pupils ?

23 B   *Interpreting survey results*

1 A survey of the popularity of subjects in the school curriculum was carried out among 21 children. The results are shown below.

Jane	Maths	David	English	Jemima	Science
Anne	History	Sunhil	Music	Pasha	Art
Tnisha	English	Adam	Maths	Yusuf	Art
Ayo	French	Jordan	Maths	Zoe	Maths
Kanika	Science	Marcus	Music	Candace	Science
Ronnie	Art	Sanjay	Maths	Rahul	History
Emma	English	Mumbi	Science	Melissa	Maths

Which subject was:

a the most popular   **b** the least popular ?

2 The pictogram on the right shows the popularity of different football teams in the premier division.

Each ball represents 100 voters.

a How many people voted for:
   i Arsenal **ii** Chelsea **iii** Spurs ?

b Which team was the:
   i most popular **ii** least popular ?

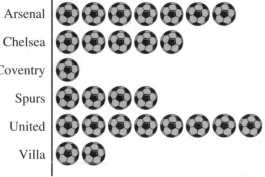

3 The bar chart on the right shows the popularity of different classical composers.

Each square represents 20 voters.

a How many people voted for:
   i Bach **ii** Grieg **iii** Handel ?

b Which composer was the:
   i most popular **ii** least popular ?

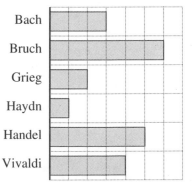

4 The block graph on the right shows the
popularity of different models of small
family car.

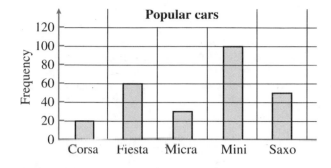

Popular cars

a How many people voted for:

   i Corsa **ii** Fiesta **iii** Micra ?

b Which car was the:

   i most popular **ii** least popular ?

5 In a survey 1000 people were asked about washing powders.

     600 indicated that they used Sudso,

     300 indicated that they used Brighto

and 100 indicated that they used Cleano.

How many of each of the three kinds of washing powder should a
supermarket order if they intend to stock in total:

a 1000 boxes   **b** 2000 boxes   **c** 100 boxes ?

6 In a survey 1000 housewives were asked which flavoured drinks
they bought for their children. Their answers were as follows:

300 bought orange   250 bought lemon   240 bought lime

100 bought raspberry   110 bought blackcurrant

A supermarket intends to stock 500 crates of these drinks.

How many crates of each flavour should they order ?

7 In a survey 500 people were asked which flavour ice-cream they
preferred. Their answers were as follows:

150 preferred vanilla   25 preferred orange   50 preferred banana

175 preferred chocolate   100 preferred strawberry

A cafe owner is going to make 100 litres of ice-cream.

How many litres of each flavour should he make ?

8 In a survey a number of people were asked which type of
pizza they would buy on their next visit to the
supermarket. The results of this survey are shown
on the pie chart. If the supermarket normally
stocks 90 pizzas, how many of each type should
be ordered ?

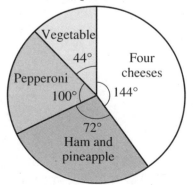

Pizza preferences

23 C   *Idea of likelihood of events*

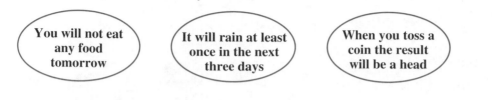

You will not eat any food tomorrow

It will rain at least once in the next three days

When you toss a coin the result will be a head

1 Look at the three statements above.

   a Do you agree that it is very **unlikely** that you will not eat any food tomorrow ?

   b Do you agree that it is very **likely** that it will rain at least once at some time during the next three days ?

   c Do you agree that when a coin is tossed it is **equally likely** that the result will be a head or a tail ?

Say whether the occurrence of the events in questions **2** to **12** is:
A very likely   **B** likely   **C** not sure   **D** unlikely   **E** very unlikely.

2 If I toss two coins together, the result will be two heads.

3 There will be snow during February next year.

4 My school bus will be a few minutes late tomorrow morning.

5 If I roll a dice, the score will be an even number.

6 If I leave my car headlights on for an hour, my car will start easily.

7 If I drive to work, all ten traffic lights on the way will be green.

8 If I throw a dice, the score will not be a six.

9 If I go jogging regularly, I will not put on weight.

10 Every day next April will be warm.

11 If I climb up a mountain, I will find that it gradually gets colder.

12 If I roll two dice, the score will be 12.

Probabilities are usually measured on a scale from 0 to 1.

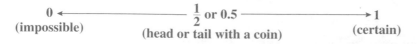

0 ← ——————————— $\frac{1}{2}$ or 0.5 ——————————— → 1
(impossible)   (head or tail with a coin)   (certain)

We say an event which **definitely will not occur** has a probability of 0.
We say that an event which **certainly will occur** has a probability of 1.

13 When you toss a coin is the probability of getting a head $\frac{1}{2}$?

14 When you pick a card from a pack of 52 cards is the probability
   a of getting a red card ?   **b** of getting a heart ?

15 Do you agree that the probability that it will snow every day for
   a week in July, in England, is 0 ?

16 Do you agree that the probability that you will **not** live until your
   150th birthday is 1 ?

17 Write down four events that are:
   a certain to occur, i.e. with a probability of 1
   b most unlikely or impossible, i.e. with a probability of 0.

Say whether the probability of the events in questions **18** to **24** is:
A 0 **B** about $\frac{1}{4}$ **C** $\frac{1}{2}$ **D** about $\frac{3}{4}$ **E** 1.

18 Passengers are told to stand upstairs in a bus.

19 I will use more petrol if I drive my car faster.

20 If I am stopped at a level crossing a train will come from the left.

21 If I throw a dice I will get an even number.

22 I will remove a blue pen from a case with 6 blue and 2 red pens.

23 The teacher chooses at random a pupil from a class of 4 boys and 12 girls. The pupil is a boy.

24 A boy will have bought his own car by his 25th birthday.

INDEX